"The older you get, the more it means."

--Bruce Springsteen

Library of Congress Control Number 2021905994

Kenneth Kaszak
How To Be Old
ISBN 978-0-9720870-3-2

valuekaszak@yahoo.com

First Printing
Printed in the United States of America

Cover Design: Andrea Djordjevic
Djordjevica263@gmail.com

Book Layout: Janeil Harricharan
blueoriontiger@hotmail.com

HOW TO BE OLD

KEN KASZAK

Elm Leaf Park Press
Pittsburgh, Pennsylvania
U.S.A.

CONTENTS

Prologue

Introduction   1

1   Chapter One   17

2   Chapter Two   27

3   Chapter Three   39

4   Chapter Four   47

5   Chapter Five   57

6   Chapter Six   79

7   Chapter Seven   95

8   Chapter Eight   103

9   Chapter Nine   109

10 Chapter Ten   121

Epilogue

PROLOGUE

The book you're about to read wasn't supposed to be written—but you're about to read it. How's that work? Let me explain.

From late February until early March of 2020 I took a trip to the eastern side of Cuba. As with any long trip, I packed reading and writing material. I make good use of my time while traveling. I had completed a story and outline for a screenplay and was making notes for three appearances at senior citizen facilities I would be doing upon my return. I also had a legal pad with notes and ideas connected to a book about the aging process.

The screenplay was going to be about a 24-year-old-man from Indiana (Terry Malloy) who lives with his widowed father. The two men share a house but are estranged. At the beginning of the story, Terry quits his warehouse job and comes to Pittsburgh. His aim is to study Performance Psychology with a well-known psychology professor at Duquesne University. The back story is that Terry was a top high school swimmer. As the swim meets got more important, and the crowds got bigger, his nervousness took over and hindered his performance in the water. In essence, he choked. He wanted to learn why this happened to him. He has an interest in coaching swimming back home and wants to learn sports psychology so that he could help others. I had tremendous passion for the project for a variety of reasons, both personal and professional.

I returned to Pittsburgh one week before the Covid-19 countywide shutdown. My intention was to write the screenplay for my competitive swimming story. The outline was complete and detailed. I knew what would happen in each scene, I knew the characters' names, I knew how they would be introduced into the story and to each other, I knew the subplots, the plot points, the pivot points, the transitions, and specific lines of dialogue. I was in love with the plot. In the story, Terry can't get into the class of the media-hungry, skirt-chasing professor (I actually met that guy) and has to find another way to conquer his fear of competing. It turns out a female psychology student (Lisa Leone) has developed a program to help individuals get over their fear of competing, performing, public speaking, etc. Lisa may or may not have left the graduate psychology program at Duquesne University because of unwanted attention from her professor.

Terry stays in Pittsburgh and enrolls in a few psychology classes. Another student from Indiana (Scott Klammer) recognizes Terry's name in the registration office and remembers him as being a rising swimming star. Terry shares his back story with Scott. Scott introduces Terry to Lisa and her "anti-choke" methods. Terry embarks on her unique program to cure "choking". One of her methods has him attend an open mic night where he gets in front of an unfriendly crowd and recites poetry. As Terry is not a poet, Ms. Leone gives him a copy of Jim Morrison's *The Lords and the New Creatures*. He ends up reciting selections of Jim Morrison poetry to a young crowd who doesn't know or appreciate the actual author. One step in getting over "performance anxiety".

Terry decides to start swimming laps in the university pool during open swim hours. The members of the university swim team do not welcome him with open arms. One team member (Dave Dowling), takes exception at an outsider in "his" pool. Dave is the good looking rich kid who happens to be a top swimmer. He's the guy we all went to college with---nicest car and prettiest girlfriend on campus. Dave and his teammates give Terry a difficult time.

Terry is not a confrontational person. His "choking" carries over to other aspects of life. He backs down from Dave Dowling's threats. Scott introduces Terry to a city-owned 20-yard indoor pool. The pool is managed by an older gentleman (Louis Brooks) who has been operating an inner-city swim program for years with little recognition or acknowledgement. He, like Lisa Leone, has developed non-traditional techniques to teach children how to swim and to enhance competitive swimmers training regimens. Mr. Brooks has come up with unique ideas on teaching and improving swimming while working with limited resources.

Every detail needed to get the story to this point was in my outline. The outline was strong. Not one weak scene. The research I did for the story focused on "Flow" psychology (you know this concept better as the "Zone"), other aspects of psychology education, the college enrollment process, and training techniques and event times for competitive swimmers. I even presented at an open mic night where I started strong but quickly bombed. I needed that experience in order to write about it *(I was surprised how quickly an open mic night audience can turn)*.

A bad ending can wreck a good screenplay and a great ending can make an average screenplay good. I had a great ending. The University of Pittsburgh holds an annual Invitational Meet in December. I had a unique way for Terry to qualify for the meet, get over his choking, enter one event, win that event (beating Dave Dowling in the process), and make amends with his estranged father. I was going to leave the reader with a hint of a burgeoning romance between Terry and Lisa. A happy, inspirational, emotional ending tied up with a ribbon. Think of *Rocky* with chlorine.

As we entered "sheltering-in-place" and schools went to online classes, I started wondering about my future, your future, and our collective future. I didn't know if college swimming would ever return to the way we've known it for decades. I thought my story—in spite of my passion for the subject—may not be relevant.

It was a difficult decision but I had to pivot. I put *Choke* aside and started to assemble the outline for this book. All in-person appearances were canceled. I had clients to deal with and the investment markets were in turmoil. I had to devote time and energy to that challenge. My swimming pool closed and it was too cold for bike rides. Shutdown mode altered my routine and my writing line-up.

I turned my attention to the research required for this book, completed the outline and wrote the manuscript. *Choke* went on the shelf.

When I wrote the book, I made the decision to write it as if we would return to a post-Covid-19 life in the near future. I don't know what that post-Covid world will be but I have to acknowledge that life has changed for us all on many levels. However, there are practices and habits we all can do that will help us age better regardless of our what is going on in the world. Non-pandemic or pandemic, the information in this book will help you age in a more productive, creative, and mentally and physically healthy way.

What you've read of the *Choke* story will probably be the last time I write anything about it. I have an interest in the subject because I have choked on many occasions. I have choked as an athlete and as a public speaker so I had extra motivation to write the script. I will not, however, ever stop thinking about the theme of the screenplay. And if I'm lucky enough to meet you, I'll let you know in advance there is a good chance I'll be talking about how good *Choke* would have been as a screenplay and a movie.

Ken Kaszak
May 2021

INTRODUCTION

"The only joy in the world is to begin."
--Cesare Pavese

If somebody told me they were going to write a book with the title *How To Be Old*, I would immediately nominate them for "Pretentious A-Hole of the Year." Who has the right—or audacity—to tackle such a subject? When I first started sharing my idea with people, I would follow by telling them that the book will be 8,000 pages long—and then I will start on the second chapter.

But once the creative process set in and I thought long and hard about the structure of the book, I saw the path to the finish. It was a day in a local coffee shop where I had the epiphany that would guide the project.

By way of introduction, I am an investment professional and a writer from Pittsburgh, Pennsylvania. It is the combination of the things I've written, the work I've been involved with, the extensive traveling I've done, and my interest in the subject of preventive health, medicine and the aging—and dying—process that put me on the path to writing this book.

The idea came to me in the spring of 2019 when I had just finished writing and self-publishing a book titled *Cut Your Calories...Now!!* That book was the culmination of a long-term self-study program of nutrition, fitness, the body-image industry, and lifestyle factors. The *Reader's Digest* story (and I realize you have to be a certain age to understand that reference) of how I became interested in those subjects began in 1992 in Gainesville, Florida. A client sent me there for six weeks to work on a real estate/banking project. I like to say that many great stories begin in bars and are fueled by alcohol. One night in a Gainesville bar I met a young woman studying gerontology at the University of Florida. It was one of the more important and long lasting "bar meetings" of my life. The subject of aging—or the study of aging—had an immediate attraction to me. From a young age, I had more than my share of ailments and injuries. I had to wear corrective shoes when I was an infant. The shoes had a bar connecting them. The purpose of the bar was to keep my feet from pointing outward. Even after I got rid of the bar, I had to wear special shoes. I had a muscle imbalance in my right eye. Even on the cloudiest day, that eye would shut. My mother took me to various doctors who tried different treatments but none of them worked.

Even as a young person, I had the thought that the two most important factors in our lives are determined before we're born—and that we have no say in the matter. One of those two factors is the combination of our physical appearance and our genetic blueprint. Think about your life and the doors opened for you—or kept shut—because of your physical appearance. I didn't choose to be born with feet that didn't work properly and a lazy eye. Although I overcame my early issues to become a good athlete, there was always somebody bigger, stronger and faster than me. When I developed my interest in the opposite sex, I also developed a face full of acne. And, to be honest, I wasn't too good looking. The girls I liked always liked somebody else.

The term "Genetic Lottery" best describes this concept. The Lottery has major impact on every aspect of our life, and our "life economics" The second important factor out of our control is the economic class we're born into. You may know of a person born into poverty who acquired great wealth. But that is the 1%. A person will die in the same economic class they are born into 99% of the time.

I returned home shortly after my chance meeting with the young woman in Gainesville. The conversation she and I had left such an impression on me that I decided to learn everything I could about nutrition, fitness, lifestyle factors and the body-image industry. Now, I will tell you that I would have failed any biology, chemistry, physiology or anatomy class I walked into. I didn't have that aptitude. What I did have was my knowledge of economic analysis and focused, razor-sharp research skills. I would learn about nutrition and the Nutrition Advice Industry (NAI) the way an economist would—with total objectivity. I had no vested interest so I could get as close to the truth as possible. My only angle would be no angle at all. I would then go on to study subjects related to nutrition.

There will be more information in upcoming chapters on my experiences in the Nutrition Trade, and the fitness and nutrition supplement industries. As for now, I will provide the insights that I acquired from my life experiences and writing projects that put me in the position to be the one to write a book with such a lofty title.

My life projects are listed before my writing projects. It is the combination of the two that put me on the journey to taking on this subject—or, better put, having the mighty subject find me.

ME:

My childhood would best be described as something out of a Norman Rockwell painting. I grew up in the Baldwin section of Pittsburgh. My parents and two brothers (and occasional dog) lived in a safe, warm, perfectly situated house. The woods and hiking paths of Elm Leaf Park were in our backyard. There was a basketball court in the valley of the park. In the winter, the borough crew would flood the court with water. There were high asphalt bumpers around the court so the water would stay on the court, freeze, and our basketball court became our ice skating rink. My brothers and I walked to school until the time we entered the eighth grade. There were two baseball fields within five minute walking distance. As a result of being a member of the baby boom, we had a lot of teammates and opponents to play any game in any sport we wanted. My father worked shifts for the gas company but always found a way to serve as the manager for our baseball teams. I may have "selective amnesia", but I can't ever remember my father missing a game as manager. My father also instilled the love of reading in his sons and took us to the library on a regular basis to borrow books.

My young life took a detour while playing football in tenth grade. I injured my leg and had severe sciatic nerve pain. The general practice doctors my parents took me to see told me to take a few days off from football practice and that I would be fine. But I wasn't fine. Sixteen months after injuring my leg I was properly diagnosed. Turns out it wasn't an issue with my leg—it was my back. I had a ruptured disk. An orthopedic surgeon told my parents that I would need a spinal fusion. The surgeon was going to shave part of my hip bone and fuse it over my L-4 and L-5 vertebra. Not a typical injury or surgery for a 16-year-old, but it was my injury and my surgery.

I had the surgery in December of my junior year in high school. The operation was a complete and total success. The intense pain I lived with daily was gone. I didn't know it right after the surgery, but the limp I was walking with would also be gone. I was in the hospital for a total of three weeks due to an adverse reaction to the anesthesia. I was going to be home schooled for the next five months but my real education came from the books I read and classic black & white movies I watched on the small TV my parents put in my room. I spent most of my time in bed. The few times I got up each day required me to put on a heavy back brace. I was given a lot of time to read books—Steinbeck, Hemingway, Ayn Rand—were digested by me during this time. The late-night movies I watched helped me develop a love of cinema. In the same way you have to be a certain age to understand the *Reader's Digest* reference, you have to be of a certain age to remember when the local TV stations used to shut down after the late, late movie. There were only four channels at the time I was recuperating from my spinal surgery. At 3:30 in the morning, there were a few different five-minute short films played before the stations signed off. The one I remember most is *High Flight*. It was footage of a jet plane taking off and flying into the clouds. Over the footage a poem, written by a Canadian aviator who died in an airplane crash, was recited. Thanks to YouTube you can watch *High Flight* right now (or, better yet, as soon as you finish reading this book).

What could have been a major negative part of my life—serious spinal surgery at a young age—ended up being a positive because of the insight it gave me, and the development of a love of movies and literature. But make no mistake—the memory of the intense pain I lived with for well over a year has never left me.

So, from a foundation of a happy, stable, loving family living in a great house with an even greater location and quick access to schools, ball fields, hiking trails, and libraries to a serious (but highly successful) back operation I started on my life's journey. Here is the path I came down:

Jobs in a gas station, a warehouse and building swimming pools to classes at the local   community college where I developed an interest in the subject of economics.

A scholarship from the state's Bureau of Vocational Rehabilitation and acceptance at Duquesne University where I proceeded to pull a 1.6 GPA my first semester (and advice from pipe-smoking Professor Marshall Levinson to return to community college).

Academic probation the rest of my time at Duquesne University (up until two weeks before graduation).

A diploma given to me during a major recession which resulted in a battle with unemployment and an endless array of ideas on how to find employment (much like the pain from my back pre-surgery, the stink of unemployment has stayed with me).

A unique job with a real estate developer who decided to open a bank in Florida near the tail end of what would become known as The S&L Scandal. It was a job that exposed me to the real estate, banking and finance industries and also gave me my first taste of travel.

The opportunity and ability to obtain an investment license while pursuing entrepreneurial avenues.

The previously mentioned experience in Gainesville, Florida, which not only spurred my interest in the aging process but also lead to a job selling exercise equipment where I started out as the guy who didn't know the difference between Standard weights and Universal weights and couldn't sell anything to anybody. But then quickly became the guy who learned the mechanics and purpose of each piece of equipment and the ability to "close" more sales than anybody in the company.

The slow—but consistent—development of an investment practice and a base of clients.

The introduction of seminars tying my interest in nutrition and fitness to my ability to find "value" through my knowledge of economics and my skills as an investment researcher.

A little bit of traction doing such programs at hospitals, corporations, non-profit groups and appearances on four radio programs.

To a major romantic "dumping" and pursuant heartbreak that crushed my spirit and put me into a major depression for a few months.

To zero traction in my nutrition and fitness presentations which required me to take a job with a bodybuilding supplement company to "keep the doors open." Without tipping my hand too much, that industry is built on hype and scam. I was good— no, great—at selling the hype and the scam. More to follow in Chapter Six.

To publishing an article in the *Pittsburgh Business Times* dealing with the subject of asset management fees which lead to obtaining a client who had just retired from a major healthcare company. This client lead to other clients and a long-term business and personal relationship. The aftermath of having that article published also got me out of the supplement industry.

To extensive traveling and the accompanying adventures and insight it provides. A detailed list of my destinations and adventures follows.

To the occasional foray into other jobs to continue to keep the doors open, most notably time spent as a laborer on an electrical contractor's crew (this is of importance to my story for one accomplishment you're about to read about).

Continued pursuit of writing projects and the development of an interest in the subject of Behavioral Finance (a.k.a. Investor Psychology) and the development of a unique class titled "How Investor Psychology Affects Us All". That class is now accredited by my state's Board of Accountancy to provide continuing education credits to CPAs and attorneys.

To the writing of *Cut Your Calories…Now!!* which leads us to where we are now—me writing this book and you reading it.

The Austrian-British philosopher Ludwig Wittgenstein once said "…my work consists of two parts: the one which is here, and everything which I have not written. And precisely this second part is the important one." You've just read a synopsis of my life in less than 2,000 words. As I look back over it, I agree with Ludwig. I presented a chronological order of my life, but things that happened to me—people I met, epiphanies that came to me, struggles I've had which can't be put into words—are as important or even more so than what you just read.

TRAVEL:

I shared that I was given the gift of travel at a young age. My journeys are a big part of who I am. A list is presented here along with some of the more unique experiences that happened along the way.

I have been to Cuba ten times, visiting the sites that are important to the Cubans, having made the acquaintance of numerous Cuban females and acquiring material and insight for three books.

Five trips to Thailand which incorporated three trips to Hong Kong and Macau (Chinese gambling capital one hour from Hong Kong).

Five trips to Europe as part of a unique art project. I became aware of a Dutch painter named Johannes Vermeer (1632 – 1675) in the mid-90s. There are 37 known paintings attributed to Vermeer and they are located in some of the top museums in the top cities in the U.S. and in Europe. I've seen them all. This project is unique for many reasons but at the top of the list would have to be the story behind the private showing I had of Vermeer's "The Music Lesson" in the basement of Buckingham Palace (side note: most people in my city don't know who Vermeer is, but the Queen of England deems his work worthy enough to have one of his painting in the Royal Collection).

Disclaimer: when I write that I've seen all 37 Vermeer paintings still in existence, there is one exception. "The Concert" was stolen from the Isabella Stewart Gardner Museum in Boston on March 18, 1990. That painting has never been recovered. The FBI still has a $10 million reward for its return and that painting, along with the other 12 pieces of artwork that were stolen, is part of one of the greatest art heists in history. While I haven't seen the "The Concert" (not yet!) I did see the frame it was taken from. To the Gardner's credit, they left the frames of the stolen paintings exactly as they were the night of the robbery.

A World War II travelogue which has taken me to Normandy, Bastogne, the River Kwai, and Iwo Jima. On my trip to the Netherlands to see the Vermeer paintings in Amsterdam and The Hauge (along with a side visit to Delft, Vermeer's hometown), I made a logistical mistake and didn't visit Arnhem and other towns connected to "Operation Market Garden." In September 1944, the Allies thought they could parachute into German occupied territory and secure nine of the bridges that would enable easy access into the northern part of Germany. The hope was that this offensive could bring the war to an end by Christmas 1944. While the attack did liberate certain Dutch towns, the main objective was not met. The story behind the planning and execution of the offensive—and the failure of military intelligence—is told in the excellent 1977 movie, *A Bridge Too Far.*

In total, I've been to 24 different countries. I've been to every American city I've wanted to see with one exception—San Francisco. While I've not been there, I do have a movie poster from the classic Steve McQueen movie *Bullitt* on my office wall. The poster is signed by every major actor and actress who appeared in the film *(I bought the piece in a store in Los Angeles from a dealer who was having cash flow problems. If I had to testify that all the signatures were authentic, I couldn't or wouldn't be able to do so).*

WRITING:

My writing began in earnest after my graduation from college and during my extended period of unemployment. I had been doing everything possible to find work: help wanted newspaper ads, employment agencies, the PA State Jobs Office, sending cover letters and resumes directly to companies. I would even go to downtown office buildings and suburban office parks and walk into various offices. There was minimal security back then; one could walk right up to the receptionist's desk and leave a resume. I once stood in front of the upscale Duquesne Club at lunchtime handing out resumes to the executives coming in for lunch. I didn't last too long—the doorman chased me away—but it was just one idea I used to find a job. So how did a bout with unemployment motivate me to write?

Around the middle of November in my graduation year, I was called by a financial services company in downtown Pittsburgh for a job interview. During my job search I only had one suit. It was a brown, double-knit polyester suit. It may have been the ugliest suit of all time but I proudly put that suit on and caught the 51D bus to downtown. I met the woman in the human resources department, interviewed with her, and she took me to another office. I then met with a gentleman who seemed to appreciate my interest in economics and finance. He told me that I would be getting a call to come back for another interview. Ah! A job before Christmas! Things were looking up for me. I did go back for a third and fourth interview and was told to expect a call after my last appearance. A job offer would have been nicer, but a call back for a fifth interview was what I was waiting for—and then maybe the job offer.

What I did receive was a "Dear Ken" rejection letter signed by the woman in the HR department. I had received at least 500 rejection letters by this point but this one really hurt because I had been told I would be called back for another interview. When I called the HR woman, she told me she would look into the matter. When she called me back, she did admit to a mix-up and invited me in for another interview. I did that one plus three others. Eight interviews but no job.

And then it came. The final rejection letter arrived two days before Christmas. The tone of the letter was offensive. The woman explained that I was no longer going to be considered for employment and that there was no mistake this time. She asked me not to contact her office.

But contact her office is exactly what I did. A few days after

Christmas, I sat down at the Smith-Corona electric typewriter my parents bought for my brothers and myself and wrote a letter to the woman in HR. I expressed my disappointment in not getting a job and my frustration with the way my interviews were handled. I told her I was treated unprofessionally and no company needs to do eight interviews for a job paying $14,400 per year. I told her that I didn't put the effort in my education and outside reading to be treated the way I was by her company. The letter was not vulgar and I didn't use offensive language but I will tell you this: if the woman from the HR department is still alive, on occasion she thinks about me.

When I put a stamp on that letter and dropped it in the mailbox, a peaceful, calming feeling came over me. All the embarrassment, frustration and anger I felt about my situation left me. At that moment in time, I realized the cathartic aspect of writing.

After the New Year, I continued just as diligently with my job search. When I would write a cover letter in response to a newspaper ad, or to a company I was applying to cold, I would pull the letter from the typewriter and reread it. I noticed that my cover letters were becoming a thing of beauty. To the point, efficient and effective in my choice of wording. Perfect sentence structure. Great openings and conclusions. Writing cover letters was helping me develop my writing skills.

It was another letter I wrote that made me realize the power of the written word. More than a year after graduating from college, after sending out untold number of cover letters and resumes, after visiting dozens of buildings passing out resumes, and doing everything else I could think of to find a job, I got one. Building swimming pools. I got the exact type of job I had before starting community college, transferring to Duquesne University, being placed on academic probation, graduating, and one year plus of unemployment. But this time building swimming pools was different. The people I worked with weren't as friendly or as interesting as the crew I had with the first job, and the quality of the product was lower than with the previous company. I also had something else the second time I didn't have the first: a college degree earned through hard work, intense study and the knowledge that I should be doing something above and beyond building swimming pools.

One of my favorite words in the English language is the word "epiphany". At a work site in the Bethel Park section of Pittsburgh one afternoon, I had an epiphany. I realized that the way I had been trying to find a job was the wrong way. People working in HR weren't going to appreciate or understand my ambition and enthusiasm for working; replying to blind ads in the newspaper weren't going to get me anywhere. The insight I acquired that day told me exactly what I needed to do.

I had developed an interest in the concept of building houses. One of the workers at my first swimming pool company talked constantly about becoming a home builder. I may have caught the ambition from him. During the time I was unemployed I never stopped my reading. I kept up to date with various real estate projects in the city and became familiar with the names of various real estate developers. I sent five cover letters and resumes to five real estate developers. I introduced myself and told each I was looking for a job in their business. Five letters went out in the mail.

One week later, I received a phone call from the secretary of a real estate developer. Her boss wanted to meet me. Two weeks after that I had a job.

Whatever I needed to write in college to pass my classes and exams, I did. But it was those two letters that I give credit to for igniting my writing passion. Beyond those two important letters, here is a list of my other writings:

How The Investment Business Really Works
2002 self-published book detailing my experiences before and since entering the investment profession and a unique look at the true workings of the business. This book was mostly written during a time when I worked the 3-11 shift on the electrical construction crew.

Under a Cuban Sky
2006 self-published book that chronicles my first trip to Cuba.

Under a Cuban Sky Segunda Parte (Part Two)
2008 self-published eBook on the second Cuba trip. Most sequels aren't as good as the first but this book is an exception to that rule.

The Confusing Muse
2011 self-published eBook that explains how I stopped making the same romantic mistakes over and over and learned a better way to deal with females. This was 100% inspired by my trips to Cuba and Thailand.

Cut Your Calories…Now!!
2019 self-published POD (Print on Demand) and eBook sharing my journey in the nutrition trade, why nutrition advice is often conflicting, and my list of 40 ways for the reader to reduce calorie consumption. It was also the spark that gave me the idea for this book.

I mentioned I had an article published in the *Pittsburgh Business Times* which resulted in obtaining many investment clients. I had another article in the PBT previous to that detailing affordable housing tax credits. I've also had 15 articles published in the *Pittsburgh Post-Gazette*. With total modesty, that number should be closer to 20. A few of the published pieces dealt with the investment business but the majority of them focused on personal experiences or the nutrition and fitness industries. I "retired" from writing pieces for the *Post-Gazette* after I submitted the most important article of the 15—a piece titled "Busy Nation". This article was a tribute to all the people who tell me how busy they are and can't get anything done but—through some miraculous occurrence—know who The Bachelor is giving the rose to and who is getting kicked off *Dancing With The Stars*. The online version of the article is titled "Are You Too Busy to Read This?" Throughout this work I will refer to some of these 15 articles.

Numerous essays for my website. Some of these should have been published in the newspaper. Thanks to the advent of websites, these pieces can be posted online. Most of these are investment related and are used to teach non-financial people the inner workings of the investment industry. As with the published articles, I will refer to some of these pieces in this book.

A non-published book of quotes. I have been collecting thoughtful, insightful, witty quotes for many years. I have used some of these quotes in various writing projects (including at the beginning of this Introduction) and I also cite them in conversation. As with my newspaper articles, quotes will be dropped into the text of this book when they fit the topic of discussion.

Lastly, I have written dozens—if not hundreds—of emails that did what they were supposed to do. Refer back to my private showing of a Vermeer painting in Buckingham Palace. When I first contacted the young woman in charge of the Royal Collection with my request via email, the reply was that there was no possible way for me to see the painting. Two heartfelt, sincere, well-structured emails later and I received an invite to cross the pond and see the painting. When people who understand art and know the legacy of Vermeer ask me how I was able to pull that one off, I tell them that it was the power of the written word.

I like to say that I have had the "Fun of Ten Men". Many of the adventures that enable me to claim that quote came as a result of emails I've written—both personally and professionally (and there are photos to prove it).

That is the introduction to me and to this book. This book— better word would be project—will actually be a trilogy. *How To Be Old*, and *How To Be Old Parts Two* and *Three*.

Part Two will be an update of my investment book. It will detail the capital markets, the inner workings of the investment industry, how one can protect themselves from "brokers gone bad," and how to structure an investment portfolio to generate income in retirement. This book will also delve into estate planning, life insurance planning, the best way to claim Social Security benefits and the pros and cons of buying annuities. We will also discuss credit scores, how to retire credit card debt and other financial issues connected to the aging process. For the record, I realized when outlining these books that, while finances are certainly an important part of being old, they are not the most important part. There are at least three things more important. Those three things will be presented in the book you are reading now.

Part Three will focus on both the mental and physical aspects of aging. What is the difference between dementia and Alzheimer's disease? Are there things to be done that can reduce the risk of losing our cognitive ability? While this book shares some insight into keeping your memory strong, *Part Three* will do it in deeper detail. People tend to have a decline in hearing as they age. Do we all suffer that decline in the same manner and at the same rate? What is actually happening inside our ear to cause the decline? What noises, sounds, letters decline first? What are the current and future types of hearing aids? Type II diabetes affects almost 10% of the population according to the Centers for Disease Control and Prevention. What can we do to decrease that percentage? If you are diagnosed with Type II diabetes, what lifestyle changes can you make to improve your health assessment? How will technology improve the aging process? *Part Three* will also detail the most effective and efficient way to deal with medical providers. There are efforts underway to increase "price transparency" in healthcare. "Surprise billing" has been part of the system for a long time and efforts are underway to eliminate it. What are those efforts? "Stem cell" therapy is getting a lot of attention and is on my radar. Let's find out if this non-invasive treatment has value to it or not. How should you choose Medicare supplements? I will find out using the same objective research that brought me to this point. Do you know what the USPSTF (United States Preventive Services Taskforce) is? Everybody should know what the purpose of that group is. Finally, I will do the research on things I am interested in (and you may be also). Why do we tend to gain weight as we age? Why does the distribution of our weight change? Do our lungs and heart lose their capacity at the same rate? What can I do to stave off the loss of heart/lung capacity? Why do our elimination functions change as we age? Is there benefit to trying to return them to the "stream of youth"? Can we ever recoup our changing and diminishing libido? Are there things we can do to keep our skin as taut as possible? Why does our height decrease as we age? We'll find out the answers to these questions—and others—together.

Before we get on with this volume, I want to share two things. I do a lot of research on—and I think about—the concept of memory, cognitive function, executive function and diseases of the brain. I know that a brain disease affecting memory and cognitive function may take years, if not decades, to develop. How this hits home to me is in my ability to type. My handwriting was so bad when I was young that my mother made me take typing classes. She bought the previously mentioned Smith-Corona electric typewriter for me and my brothers to practice typing on—so she said. I think she actually bought it for her middle son because my handwriting was just so bad.

Many of the things that happened to me and that I have shared so far happened to me because of my ability to write. But as I write these words now, I wonder if 5, 10, 15 years from now I'll lose my ability to type. Will I forget that my ring finger goes up slightly to the left to type the "w" key? Will I no longer know that I take my right index finger to the lower left to type a "n"? Because this is on my mind and I don't know if or when it will occur, I want to get this trilogy finished as soon as possible.

I know some people who appear to have the "Perfect Life". They received a winning ticket in the Genetic Lottery and they were born into stable families. They grew up knowing their grandparents and were athletically inclined. They had no great tragedies in their young lives and obtained a good education and a good job. They had just the right amount of experience in the romance department before finding their life partner. They were comfortable in their careers. They made a good living and ended up with a stable retirement. They didn't have any major artistic or business aspirations, as the majority of those don't become fulfilled. When there has been a family death, it came in the proper order of things. Some of these individuals are now grandparents. As they accumulate more years, they will enjoy good health, remain active, and see their grandchildren grow up. And then, one night in the future, after having lived a complete life, they will kiss their wife or husband good-night with the same passion as their first kiss, go to sleep and not wake up. The perfect exit for the Perfect Life.

While I've known people who seemingly had this life—or are in the midst of it— few of us will have it. Most of will have—or had— challenges, detours, obstacles, and ambitions not achieved that take away from The Perfect Life. Some of us will have difficulties early. We will have issues with our family structure, employment, romance, and our business or artistic ambitions. We will be defined by what we overcome. We will try to be consistent with our professional and personal lives and endure the tough parts but celebrate each accomplishment and victory. It's a purpose of this book to make the accomplishments more pronounced and to lessen the tough parts.

Let's get on with it and figure out *How To Be Old* together.

And—in case you're wondering—I still have the Smith-Corona electric typewriter. It is a prized possession of mine.

How To Be Old

CHAPTER ONE

Quotes & Stats and a Note About Time
(bur first—two stories)

I want to open this book with two stories. They are relevant to the subject and are related to a number of things you will be reading about shortly.

<u>Story One</u>
I am a swimmer and a bicycle rider. I swim at a local non-profit fitness facility. Because of my writing and the ventures I'm involved in, some employees at this facility know me. I usually swim early in the mornings but I found myself in the building late one afternoon. At the front desk, the manager, Brandon, was talking to a woman. Brandon and I talk on a regular basis and I told him about this project even before I started working on the outline. The woman he was talking with was not a member of the facility but had a membership elsewhere. She thought her outside membership entitled her to admission. Brandon was explaining why it didn't and, as he's supposed to do, was trying to sell her a membership at his location. He saw me standing at the other end of the counter and thought there was a way I could help close the sale. He introduced me to the woman, told her what I did for a living, and then shared that I would be writing a book titled *How To Be Old*.

The woman turned to look at me and said, "Oh, I know how to be old. You get your hair colored, you try new styles, you work out twice as much and you get plastic surgery. I think I look pretty good for 54." Now, I will share that I've seen various women of various ages in various stages of dress and undress. When she made that remark, I could feel a sentence forming in my voice box. That remark was going to be, "Well, let's hope there's at least one guy that thinks so." But my polite filter took over. It would have been a rude comment and may have cost Brandon a sale, so that woman never heard that statement. But she had an issue, and that issue was that she equated the aging process only with the physical aspects. If finances are not even in the top three in order of importance for aging well, your physical appearance may not even crack the top five.

Story Two

While I was once in a nine-year relationship, I've had various experiences with females before and after. One day I was going to meet a woman for lunch. She was an attractive, fit, well-traveled female who was a runner and a cyclist. The restaurant we were meeting at was in a shopping center called Caste Village in the South Hills of Pittsburgh. I should share that this woman is three years older than me.

I drive a six-speed Jeep. I pulled into the parking lot and was on the phone with one of my clients. I parked, got out of the Jeep, and walked to the restaurant while finishing the call. My date looked great. We were having a cozy lunch date. She had drawn a picture for me. It was a picture of an onion. I am a fan of all onions and have a colorful matted and framed painting of onions on the wall in the kitchen. Her drawing was a gift to me.

My phone rang. It was the local police department. An officer on the phone told me that my Jeep was "…rolling across the parking lot." What the…? I excused myself and ran outside. A small crowd had gathered around the police car. What had happened was that I left the vehicle in neutral when I got out. When I walked into the restaurant, the Jeep rolled a few feet forward and lightly tapped the bumper of the car parked opposite. When the driver got into that car and started to back up, the Jeep "rolled" a few feet with her car.

I backed the Jeep up and got out to look at the other car. The officer looked with me. There was no scratch. No damage. The owner of the car was an older woman who stood to the side. The officer told her he didn't see any scratch. "I don't know about this," the woman said. "My husband may want to investigate." The officer told us to exchange contact information. I handed her my driver's license. When she handed me her license, I looked at it and did an immediate and neck-jarring double take. The woman probably knew the reason for the double take. This grey-haired, wrinkled, frail-looking woman was ACTUALLY YOUNGER THAN ME.

Now, what was going on? A woman older than me was waiting in the restaurant and looked great. A woman younger than me looking less than great. I don't know if the woman in the parking lot had terrible tragedies in her life, an unhappy home life, children that created a lot of "quick aging" stress or had survived disease, but my thought process is that what she looked like—what any of us look like—is most likely 75% attributed to the Genetic Lottery and 25% to lifestyle factors and things that happen to us after our parents bless us with their genes. And even though the "body-image" industry, the fitness industry, and the supplement industry are constantly trying to sell new products in an attempt to convince you that they can overcome the Genetic Lottery—they can't. I learned that early on in my study and you need to learn it, too.

After the incident in the parking lot, I was convinced I was going to receive a phone call from the husband telling me they needed a new front end and a wheel alignment. But that call never came.

One of these two women will resurface later in this book. Stay tuned for her return.

Quotes

We've heard them for a long time—and others similar in nature: "Age is nothing but a number." "You're as young as you feel." To these quotes—and others like them—I call nonsense. You are the age you are. You are the number and the age equal to the number of times you've blown out candles on birthday cakes. The Life Extension Industry will tell you there is a chronological age and a biological age, but it's just one of many ways to separate you from your money. I'm not going to provide any numbers to delineate what age is old, what age is on the cusp, and what age is young. I know people in their upper 70s who are still active and still creating and achieving things. Inversely, I know some people who were "curmudgeonly" before they turned 40.

Here are some quotes I prefer:

"It's not how old you are—it's how you are old."
--Rocker and hunter Ted Nugent

"The two most important days in your life are the day you are born and the day you find out why."
--Mark Twain

"Don't live the same year 80 times and call it a life."
--Robin Sharma (with a bit of editing)

"The only way not to get old is to die young."
--*Route 66*, Season 2, Episode 3
"Goodnight Sweet Blues"

"No one here gets out alive."
--James Douglas (Jim) Morrison

My favorite aging quote comes from a little-known movie titled *The Angriest Man in Brooklyn* starring Robin Williams and released on a limited basis shortly before his death. The premise: Williams' character has a terminal disease but he is given incorrect information that he will die within 90 minutes. He races around Brooklyn trying to make amends with people in his life and to come to terms with his estranged son. He is able to accomplish these items. At the end of the movie he is in a hospital bed with his son sitting bedside. He knows he is going to die and is prepared for the end. He says to his son (paraphrasing), "I know my tombstone will read 1951 dash 2014. But it is the dash that will be the most important part." Truer words never spoken—in a movie or in life.

Statistics

Due to the ventures I'm involved in, I read (and love to collect) interesting and relevant statistics. A female born in 1900 had a life expectancy (LE) of 48.3 years; a man's LE was 46.3 years. The blended rate is currently 78.6 years. Not only did we increase LE by two-thirds in 120 years, we increased it by 7.8 years just since 1970. While the Life Extension industry, the supplement industry, and the medical industry will all stand up and take credit, the real credit belongs to the public health sector, the pharmaceutical industry, and capitalism.

Vaccinations have eliminated diseases of childhood, antibiotics provide a cure for infections that used to be fatal. Calvin Coolidge's son died in 1924 after developing a blister on his foot that became infected. He was playing tennis on the White House courts while wearing shoes with no socks—something many of us have done a thousand times. The sepsis that killed the 16 year old would have been prevented today by a simple course of antibiotics.

The public health sector made our world cleaner and did an amazing job in reducing the number of cigarette smokers. In 1965, over 40% of the adult population smoked. In 2017, that figure was down to 14% (down from 15.5% just one year earlier). A major killer—cigarette smoking—was reduced to the point that to see somebody light up a cigarette now is an anomaly whereas it once was the norm.

Capitalism helped increase life expectancy by something we all take for granted now—the refrigerator. The safe storage of food and the accompanying decrease of diseases caused by spoiled or highly cured food added to our LE. Automobile safety, workplace safety, and a decrease in violent crime have all added to increased years. Those years came about due to a combination of business, government, and public health measures.

Because of increased life expectancy, we are an old country. While 9.3% of the world's population was over 65 years of age in 2020, per the United Nations Population Division, 16.6% of the U.S. population was over 65 in 2020. During 2020, an estimated 10,800 Americans turned 65 years of age *every day*. By 2029, that number will increase to 11,500 according to the U.S. Government Accountability Office. In 2030, for the first time ever, there will be more U.S. citizens over the age of 65 than under the age of 18 (Source: U.S. Census Bureau). According to the Social Security Administration, there is a 48% chance that at least one half of a 65-year-old married couple will live to age 90.

As an investment professional, I've been dealing with Required Minimum Distributions (RMDs) for a long time. The RMD is the percentage of qualified assets (i.e., IRAs, 401(k)s, SEPs) that must be distributed beginning in the year (with minor exception) that an individual turns 72 years of age (up from age 70.5 in 2019). Life expectancy tables estimate a person reaching 72 will live for 16 more years. Each year, the percentage of the RMD increases. If you live to be 100, the percentage of IRA assets that must be distributed equals 16% of the account balance as of December 31st of the previous year (I still run into people who think once you reach a certain age you don't have to worry about RMDs and you don't have to pay income taxes. Unfortunately, that's not true).

In my city and county, the aging of the population is pronounced. Data from 2018 listed the percentage of Americans over the age of

65 at 15.8%. The County of Allegheny, which includes the City of Pittsburgh, had a population over the age of 65 of 18.9%. My theory for the advanced age in my county can be traced back to the recession of 1981-1982. We had numerous steel mills and other industrial companies that shut down. People had to leave this area to get jobs. I had many friends from high school who took off for Houston, Texas, where employment was plentiful. One of those friends once told me they had a Halloween party one year and invited everybody from the South Hills of Pittsburgh who was living in Houston. The guest roster totaled 39.

So those fellows—young guys when they left Pittsburgh but grandfather-age now, didn't have children in Pittsburgh. The children they didn't have here aren't here to have children of their own and the result is an average age significantly above the national average.

A Note About Time

When I was a child, my mother's oldest sister told me that as you get older, the years go by faster. At the time, the school year seemed to last forever but so did summer. When I was in college and saddled with a 1.6 GPA and academic probation, each semester was an eternity. But as I got older, I realized that what my aunt (she was Serbian so she was my "Tetie") told me was true. Time does go by faster—with one major exception which I'll share at the end of this chapter.

I think of time in different ways. When I think that my life went by fast to this point, I stop and think back to my childhood, my time in school, the different careers I had, the numerous people I've associated with, the places I've traveled to, and the items I've written. What seems like a life that has gone by quickly doesn't seem so quick when I think about my pre-teen years, my teen years, my 20s, 30s, 40s, and so on. My life is the exact time it took to live it.

Another way I think about time is this: even though I've done many interesting things and have creative works to show for it, I've wasted a lot of time. I think back to the time I spent in nightclubs and bars (my "ballroom days"), the time I spent not creating, the time I spent in jobs where I was ridiculously underemployed (one does have to generate income so I took what I could get) and the people I spent time with who—upon reflection—I realized contributed to my wasted time. But I also have to realize that my persona, my insights, my knowledge, my experiences and my writings would not be what they are if I didn't invest (a nicer way to say "waste") that time.

I also think about the headache I get when somebody I have to deal with cries to me about how busy they are. My 15th and final article published in the *Pittsburgh Post-Gazette* was titled "Busy Nation". It is a tribute to the people who can't get things done yet somehow know who The Bachelor is giving the rose to and always have the time to watch the Steelers pre-game show, the game itself and then the post-game show. The article details the "politics of busyness," details where "busy" people are often employed, and why these people are not so busy but just inefficient managers of their time.

Someday Never Comes is the title of a great John Fogerty song and also an adage I use all the time. "Ken, someday I'm going to write a book," or "Ken, someday I'm going to get a passport and travel like you," or "Ken, someday I'm going to buy a bike and ride around town like you." I have heard (and continue to hear) this on a constant basis from people who tell me what they are going to do—someday. But to those people—and millions more like them—who plan to do something "someday" that day never comes.

My first introduction to the adage came from my Tetie—the same one who informed me that the years pass by faster the older you get. Before I was 10 years old, she told me that she was going to write a book about our family coming from the old country (Serbian province of Yugoslavia) and getting established in Pittsburgh. There were numerous interesting stories, many of which originated from the fact my grandfather owned a small pool room and my grandmother was once busted for booking numbers (whose Buba *didn't* do that?!). I did know my grandfather's brother (who had the cool name of Bronko) was accused of cheating in a card game in a house on Sarah Street. The accuser took out a gun and killed him. Bronko was 27 years old (maybe he was the first of the 27 Club with membership including Jim Morrison, Jimi Hendrix, Kurt Cobain, Janis Joplin and Amy Winehouse!). So, when my Tetie announced she would write this book, I was both excited and proud.

As I got older and would see my Tetie, she would talk about writing the book "...as soon as I get my house clean." This went on for years. She had a small house. I graduated from high school and then college and that book was waiting to be written—as soon as there was a clean house to write it in. When I learned the word "eccentric" I realized my aunt was a textbook example. She was highly opinionated, held grudges from things that happened decades ago and gave many of her unusual ways to her two adopted children. The only step I'm aware she took toward writing her book was enrolling in a Word Processing class at the University of Pittsburgh where she worked.

When I wrote my first book and self-published it, she told me that it was now her turn to write her book. But she passed away without doing so and without getting that house clean.

I do think about my Tetie when I realize how many months of a new year have passed or how quickly the previous month flew by. And here is the reason why I think about her and what she said to me: a famous person was once being interviewed. I will reveal this person's identity in a few paragraphs. The interviewer asked this person if it seemed like their career went by quickly. The famous person shook his head and said something like, "It seems like it went by so fast...like having a cup of coffee."

The famous person then paused and said, "But I don't mind that. Cause if you think about it, the only time that time goes slow is when you're having difficulties in life." Just like Robin Williams' character talking about the "dash" at the end of the movie, these words registered with me. So true. Time crawls when you're having problems. I want my time to fly by. I'll gladly take that over the days that drag, the nights without sleep and the horrible feeling in my chest cavity that results when stress hormones are being pumped out.

Who was this great philosopher? It is one of my favorite people who happens to be from Beaver Falls, PA. Joseph William Namath. Joe Namath. Few people have had a life as interesting and full as that man. I was always a fan; when he made his comment about time passing quickly vs. slowly, I became an even bigger fan.

Thanks to the wonders of YouTube, I recently watched video of Joe playing in his last football game—not for the New York Jets but for the Los Angeles Rams. It wasn't right seeing Joe in that non-Jets uniform. It was sad to see him hobbling on bad knees trying to avoid being sacked. Joe was old for a football player, 34, but young for a man. I'm glad that he was able to establish a career after his football days and do good deeds. He wrote an excellent book about his football and personal life (*All the Way: My Life in Four Quarters*) and has been open and honest about his alcohol and concussion issues. I've always said that he should be the only person on this planet allowed to put his right index finger in the air to let us know who is Number One. Super Bowl III may be the greatest—and most important—professional football game ever played.

I'll end this chapter with a Joe Namath story. Beaver Falls is a rival to Aliquippa. Both ex-mill towns, both producers of great athletes, both made up of various ethnic groups. I've been to Aliquippa many times. On one of my visits I wanted to buy a "Quippa" ski cap. I went into Boulevard Sports. The owner of the shop had framed photos of himself with different sports personalities on the wall, including a few with Joe Namath. Joe was at an age where he still looked like Joe Namath, had good hair and his perfect smile. He was wearing a Navy blue suit with a purple and white patterned tie. The bald-headed store owner was also in the photo, with his hair still intact. I have a Navy blue suit. I looked for a purple and white tie and I tried to find one that resembled the tie Joe was wearing in the photo. I found one; it wasn't exact but it was close enough.

The next time I needed to suit up, I put on a crisp, white shirt with my new tie and my Navy suit. I checked my look in the mirror before leaving the house.

Oddly enough, I didn't look quite as good as Joe did in his suit and tie. While I pulled a good ticket in the Genetic Lottery, Joe Willie pulled a perfect one (of course, the tie wasn't a perfect match...)

How To Be Old

CHAPTER TWO

The Most Important Chapter in 'How To Be Old'

If finances aren't in the top three of importance in growing old, and physical appearance doesn't crack the top five, what could number one be? It's this: **you must live your life the way a writer lives their life**. It's so far ahead of numbers two through ten that I want you to envision Joe Namath running off the field after Super Bowl III holding his index finger up in the air. That day, the New York Jets were number one. From this day forward, living your life the way a writer lives their life should be number one. I'll explain in detail why living your life this way is at the top of the list.

If you go back to the Introduction chapter and reread all the things I've done, and the places I've been, they all happened to me because of my ability to write. I took advantage of the ancillary benefits writing provides—along with the cathartic benefits—to see the world, have interesting adventures, and survive in the investment industry. I didn't learn to write in high school, community college or at Duquesne. My writing ability was honed from writing cover letters, a highly cathartic letter to a certain woman in the HR department of a certain company, a letter sent to five real estate developers which resulted in one job and then onto the first motion picture screenplays I wrote (two of which received small grants from the PA Council on the Arts). My creative soul came to me as a direct result of unemployment and the struggle to change that status.

When I became serious about writing, I was greatly influenced by a quote I came across. The quote was attributed to the great English poet and painter William Blake (1757–1827). "The road of excess leads to the palace of wisdom." I read that Jim Morrison of The Doors was a major fan of Blake's work. I took that quote—and Jim's endorsement—to mean that a writer must engage in decadent and excessive behavior and that the behavior should be fueled by substance. And my choice of substance was alcohol.

I drank and I drank and then I drank some more. I spent a lot of time in bars and clubs. I went there for two reasons: they had alcohol and it was where the females were. While I walked out of bars and clubs solo far more often than I did with female company, the times I left with somebody happened enough time for me to think that it could happen any night that I was out and about.

I came to respect my hangovers. I would wake up with what I came to call a "literary hangover" thinking my headache and upset stomach were somehow going to help my writing. I would take my Tylenols, eat a baloney and cheese sandwich and wait for the hangover to subside so I could drink again. If William Blake's quote helped Jim Morrison write songs, it was going to help me write screenplays.

But then a fellow named Bruce Springsteen came along. Bruce was writing great songs and working out in the gym. He was putting out album after album of songs that will be listened to forever and he was looking healthy and strong. I had to reexamine William Blake's quote.

Maybe "excess" had little or nothing to do with drinking, drugging and cavorting. Maybe the quote was saying if you develop passion for something and put your time and effort into it, you will be delivered to a place—the palace of wisdom—where your passion could pay benefits. Springsteen's road of excess was sitting in his room as a young man honing his guitar skills and then his songwriting skills.

When I realized that the road of excess does not have to be paved with substance abuse, it was a life changer for me. While I had been an above average athlete before my spinal surgery, I had gotten away from a healthy lifestyle. I was smoking cigarettes, drinking more than I should and avoiding exercise. For a guy who grew up in a neighborhood where it was possible to play three different sports in the same day, my lack of physical activity was the opposite of what my young life would have predicted. To quit my cigarette habit, I started swimming laps at the Duquesne University pool. I remember my first time in the pool. I could only do 11 lengths—one at a time. When I showered and got dressed, I walked out in the cold night air and lit a Newport. My lungs objected to the workout I had just put them through and the cigarette smoke I was inhaling. My lungs were telling me "one or the other—you can't have both." I chose swimming. And I owe a major "thank you" to Bruce Springsteen for getting me started on a life of increased physical activity and healthy lifestyle choices. I owe a "thank you" to both Bruce and Jim Morrison for motivating me to express my creative soul.

The Cathartic Aspects of Writing

I've shared one of many ways that I've benefitted from the cathartic aspects of writing. I got this benefit before I really knew how to write. Once I learned to write I took full advantage of the ancillary benefits of writing. Above all else, these benefits are the reason you want to live like a (physically active and fit) writer.

Before I list the ancillary benefits of writing, let me share the two most important things you must do in order to write. The first is this: develop 100% total objectivity. Give up your opinions. Let every thought you have pass through your brain's "objectivity filter" before committing it to paper or speaking it in conversation. Total objectivity is a must. You will not write anything of any relevance or importance unless you acquire it. Most beginning writers—myself included—thought that what we were writing was good—for no other reason than we wrote it. It wasn't until I acquired total objectivity that I could begin to write quality material. It wasn't easy for me to become objective as I come from a long line of opinionated, conclusion-jumping people. My father and uncles used to sit around a table drinking beer, pouring shots ("shooters" they called them), smoking cigarettes and cigars, and throwing out their respective opinions on subject after subject. As a young person, when my father or one of my uncles made a declarative statement on a subject such as work, cars, money, business, life—or another family member—I took it to heart. I thought it was gospel. Most of us are the end products of our physical appearance, the socio-economic class we grew up in, our education, our intelligence (which is different than education), our experience and the influence of our families. Those factors make it even more difficult to acquire objectivity but, in order to write, it must be done.

When I say you must give up your opinions, the dissenters in the crowd will say, "Wait a minute. Everybody is entitled to their own opinion." Not true. If that opinion is based on incorrect facts, are you still entitled to it? If that opinion is based on biased behavior, are you still entitled to it? Nope. If you suffer from "limitation bias" (the basic inability to understand a concept or the lack of knowledge of a subject), how can your opinion have any merit? If your opinion comes from something you heard your drunk uncle say when your mind was super impressionable, what is the value of that opinion? Zero.

It's important to distinguish between opinions and insights. Insights come from experiences and objective thinking. I had obtained a hard-to-get Series 7 license to sell securities. I had opinions on how the investment business worked but I couldn't sell a thing. It wasn't until I acquired my insights into the business that I was able to get clients. I had opinions into how the male/female "dance" should go. And I got my heart stepped on many times. It wasn't until I acquired my insight into the dance that I had positive, happy and numerous encounters with the opposite sex. Opinions have no value, insights have tremendous value.

The second thing you must do in order to write is acquire "The Bell". The Bell was introduced to me in John Fogerty's tremendous autobiography, *Fortunate Son*. Fogerty credits the songwriter Hoagy Carmichael with introducing him to the concept. The Bell is that tiny alarm that goes off in your brain when something you've thought of for your book, screenplay, article, business plan, love letter, poem, etc., just does not belong. If you don't have The Bell you will put on paper almost anything that comes into your brain. It's not easy to get The Bell but you must have it—and you will only get it after acquiring total objectivity.

The school of music at Indiana University in Bloomington, Indiana is named after Hoagy Carmichael. A well-known resident of Bloomington once made a statement that involves The Bell. Between 1980 and 1991, John Mellencamp released nine studio albums. These albums contained many songs that will be listened to for eternity. John was being interviewed after releasing one of these albums and he said something to the effect that "...the more you do it, the easier it becomes." I was floored when I read that. The guy writing some of the best songs ever was saying it was getting easier for him. He wasn't complaining about running out of material and he wasn't talking about how difficult it was for him to keep producing quality songs. He was saying it was getting easier for him. That comment by John stuck with me for a long time until, after acquiring more years and more experience writing in different formats, I understood what he was saying. He was saying that The Bell prevented things that don't belong in a song from ever getting close to his brain. When I started to write, I wrote some things that were amateurish and embarrassingly silly. I didn't have The Bell. When I developed total objectivity, The Bell came with it. My writing improved tremendously. The amateurish and embarrassing passages disappeared.

The Ancillary Aspects of Writing

This list is extensive. Long after I finish presenting it, I will still be thinking of new benefits to add to the list.

The number one benefit from the number one item you must do to age well is this: by acquiring total objectivity you will also acquire **the ability to learn things above your level of intelligence.** The only reason I have an investment practice is because I was able to learn complicated subject matter above my level of intelligence. Don't forget: I'm the guy who had to take and pass remedial math just to enter community college. I'm the guy who had a 1.6 GPA my first semester at Duquesne University (and I'm sure a teacher or two gave me a "C" just for showing up every class). The reason I've been able to write on a variety of subjects is strictly due to the objectivity I acquired when learning to write.

The ability to learn above our respective levels of intelligence is vital as we age. Think about all the information the healthcare industry, the insurance industry, the investment industry and the retirement industry, et al., will be throwing at you. Think of all the scammers who are out there trying to separate you from your money. Your opinions and biased behavior aren't going to help you out. Only your objectivity will be there to guide you in your decision making. The ability to keep learning (and the importance of it) may have protective effects from dementia as we will learn in Part Three of this series.

Here are other ancillary benefits of writing:

Improved Memory

My memory is strong. I have to maintain various investment statistics, financial history, information on nutrition and fitness, quotes, client histories, and experiences from my travels in my current memory (my term). Because of my age and the ventures I am currently involved in or was involved in the past, I know a lot of people. Add this to all my childhood experiences, school era experiences, etc., and I have a lot of information stored. Much of that information is of a type that may need to be recalled at any time.

My memory—and the ability to recall facts, figures, quotes, memories—is strong due to the writing I've done and continue to do.

Improved Research Skills

A great quote by English physician Will Harvey (1578- 1657) asks, "What is research but a blind date with knowledge?" A significant portion of my life is doing research—getting as close to the truth as possible. Writing makes the required research much more effective and efficient. You're going to be presented with options on insurance, finances, and health care decisions going forward. And these decisions will be more important with the more birthdays you have. A writing lifestyle will give you better research skills to assist in making better decisions.

Editing Ability

Writing will make you a better editor. I'm not only talking about editing written documents; I'm talking about editing "the noise of life". We all have entities vying for a piece of our time (and our money). It's important to edit time wasting/no value entities from your life. I have to maintain a regular reading schedule of financial and healthcare newsletters, blogs and books. I have a finite list that is reviewed periodically. When I am approached by an entity that wants to put something on my plate, I know in short order whether or not they have value and deserve space on the plate. Usually not, and they are dispatched immediately. When I do find a newsletter or blog or book that adds value above and beyond what is currently on my plate, they get added. *Of course, the more you write the better of an editor you become. That editing ability will only arrive once you achieve total objectivity.*

Dealing With People

Earlier we got rid of the old adage, "Everybody is entitled to their opinion." We're about to send another one to the cleaners. You may think we're all unique characters and we're all independent thinkers. So not true. The truth is that with most people you meet, you've met them before. You may not know everybody's birthday and favorite Sinatra song but, by their intelligence, motivations, views of the world and opinions, you've dealt with a similar character type before. Just like in literature or screenwriting, there is a finite number of types of characters in this world (it is rare to come across a truly unique character; I've been lucky in my travels to meet more than a handful). In my world, I have to ascertain quickly what type of personality I am dealing with. My writing ability has given me the skills to do just that.

Enhanced Listening and Conversation Skills

Do you know a person who, when you're having a conversation with them, is not really listening or concentrating on what you're saying, but instead is thinking of what they will say next? I know many. I may have been one at some point. But my writing history has given me the ability to listen with more focus. And, given that we know there are a finite number of characters running around, I know how to reply to them based on their character type. In conversation, many people—young and old—go into "Repeat Mode". They tell you something and then a few moments later repeat the same thing. This happens a lot when people are inebriated but I've been on the receiving end of it from non-inebriated people. If I ever was in Repeat Mode (inebriated or not), it was long ago and it is thanks to my writing background that I left the RMC (Repeat Mode Club). A writing lifestyle makes one better at speaking in front of groups and in one-on-one encounters.

More Effective Meetings

A meeting should follow Stephen King's Three Rules of Writing. (1) Make it clear: what is the purpose of the meeting?, (2) Use your own words: say what you know, what you need to find out and what you want to accomplish and (3) Delete needless words. Don't talk about something just because it may have some vague connection to the meeting subject. As my writing increased and improved, I noticed I was able to get clients and potential clients on the learning curve and push them up the curve more efficiently. One of the biggest wasters of time in the business and non-profit world is meetings. But not for people who write.

The Technology Learning Curve

This is connected to Learning Things Above Your Level of Intelligence but I had to list it separately for personal reasons. Think of all the technology that has been—and will continue to be— introduced. Much of this technology will make your life better. I used to be the guy afraid of computers. I had a slow computer. It wasn't old and it was made by a well known company. I would see ads online placed by companies who said they could make computers faster. I would contact these companies and they each told me something different than the previous one. A fellow came to my office and put a RAM stick in the side of the computer. His promise that it would be faster did not come true. And I was out $60. Another fellow sat at my desk for a few hours doing things on the computer. When he left with $80 of my money, he told me the computer would be faster. Not so. Another fellow actually took my hard drive, went away for a few days and returned with it, telling me the computer would now be faster. Of course, it wasn't. $100 wasted.

It wasn't until I met a computer geek (using that term with respect) named Steve that I realized my issue. I told him what computer I had. He showed me a chart revealing I had the slowest processor on the market. My processor (didn't know what that was or the importance of it until I met Steve) was doing 950 functions per second. Steve sold me a floor model desktop with a processor doing 5,500 processes per second. I faced my fear about computers and advanced up the learning curve. Now, those fellows who came to my office and took my money knew something I didn't know. My processor speed. There wasn't anything they were going to do to my computer that was going to make it operate faster. Since I met Steve my technical difficulties have been minimized.

I now have a camera, microphone, wireless devices, printers, an external hard drive, and USB hubs for my office. As new technology is introduced, we're all going to have to decide if it provides value—makes our existence more effective and efficient—and acquire it, acquire it in the future after a price drop, or if we don't need it.

One of my favorite quotes about technology is credited to Howard Stern. Howard said on his show one day that (paraphrasing) "I know I'm going to die one day but I'm going to be pissed about it because of all the new technology I'll miss."

A Longer "Split-Second"

"Your car is shot," "You're fat...and ugly," "You have 11 cavities," "You're still fat."

When we hear unpleasant or emotional news, we tend to reply with the first thing that comes into our head. Likewise, when we receive bad news we open up the doors for stress hormones to start pumping, our breathing to change and gloom and doom to begin. It's done in a split second. It's our natural and normal reaction. The more I wrote, the more I realized that when somebody told me something negative or argumentative, that the split-second was lengthened. Before my stress hormones kicked in, I was able to objectively (there's that word again) and calmly decide what my reaction was going to be. There is a percentage of people who don't react emotionally to bad or disturbing news. But if you don't have that "coolness" naturally, thinking and living like a writer is your best chance of acquiring it.

Your Own Personal "BS" Detector

Think about the reach of the investment, insurance, fitness, lifestyle, and body-image industries. Think of all the products and services they are marketing. Think how they would love to separate you from your money and give you no value in return. My BS detector is razor sharp and is always on. I use it every day in the ventures I'm involved in and with the people I meet. This benefit is used not just for the overt BS thrown at me but also for the embellishment, subtle and diversionary BS so common in the business world. I saved this benefit for next to last but it is one of the most important benefits I've obtained from writing. Want your own BS detector? Then start writing.

Better Time Management Skills

While all the ancillary benefits are important, this one has a sweet spot in my heart. I will reintroduce my final article for the *Pittsburgh Post-Gazette*, "Busy Nation". Too much of my work time is spent dealing with individuals who have to tell me how busy they are. I'm a person trying to create, achieve, and accomplish in this world and I have to deal with people who don't have the time to learn the value of what I offer. My time management skills came to me directly as a result of writing. Even though I have a lot of things going on at any given time, I still find time to do something vital to anybody with a creative soul: absolutely nothing. I have time to let my creative soul run where it wants to. I can keep up with my work responsibilities, my reading and writing schedule, my physical activity, my enjoyment of movies, my social activities and still have time to do nothing.

When I come across some residents of Busy Nation and they start their diatribe of being "so busy" I send them a copy of my article via email. The ironic thing is that I have many clients who own businesses or have high ranking positions in the medical industry. I never hear from them how busy they are. They too have a lot going on but figured a way to get it done. As for me, I would be embarrassed to tell another human being "I'm so busy." But it is not a source of embarrassment for the people who wear it as a badge of honor.

Before providing this list of ancillary benefits, I shared there is a cathartic aspect to writing. The fact that I wrote the article and it was published in the newspaper is a perfect example of a cathartic aspect of writing. Just knowing it's out there, and available to send to a resident of Busy Nation, provides me peace of mind. If you're a resident of Busy Nation and want to leave, it's easy. Start living life the way a writer does.

"Training Your Brain"

Now that you have been exposed to the many benefits of writing, and understand the importance of objective thinking, there are a few more principles you must adopt that will help deliver those benefits faster. You must "train your brain" to think like a writer. This includes objective, non-emotional thinking but also includes letting your subconscious do the heavy lifting. Your creative soul works best when you are living your life, doing your daily chores and thinking of nothing. I break creative thinking into two parts: focused and unfocused. Focused creativity is when you have loaded your subconscious with specifics of a screenplay, non-fiction book, short story, article, essay, poem, business plan or love letter you are working on. Every so often an idea, a piece of dialogue, an addition to the text will pop into your mind. As you get deeper into the outline process, you will realize what exact details—or problems—you need to solve to finalize your outline. You will "reload" your subconscious with these details and become even more focused. This heightened focus can be considered a form of self-brainstorming.

Unfocused creativity is part of every creative person's soul. They go through life wondering if everything they see, are told, or read can be the basis of a book or screenplay or some other creative output. Everything you read, and every movie you watch started with a writer hearing something, seeing something, reading something, or recalling some experience and asking themselves "What if?"

"Refraining Your Brain"

Two of the articles I've had in the *Post-Gazette* dealt with my love of baseball growing up and the positive impact baseball has had on me. When I was young, baseball was everything. We played it from spring to fall. In the winter I would read biographies of famous players. When the Pittsburgh Pirates went to spring training in February, I didn't care how cold it was in Pittsburgh because there were stories to read about that year's team, the rookies who had a shot at making the team, and personal stories of the players and their families. It also meant that sign-ups for the North Baldwin Baseball Association were soon to follow.

But for the importance of baseball in my early life, here is a stunning confession: I can no longer watch the sport. It is too slow and too boring. The game has always been that way but I have changed. My attention span—and yours—has been crushed. It's a combined result of 400+ television stations to choose from, plus the streaming services, plus the computer we walk around with in our pockets that demands our attention every few minutes. I also have a bigger plate and more on it than when I was much younger.

Technology is the writer's friend and foe. It is your friend because it makes the actual writing much easier. When I started to write screenplays, it was on the much-used Smith-Corona electric typewriter. I had to learn where the components of a screenplay went on the page and then set the tabs to those places. Unlike a simple word processing program on a computer, there was no highlighting and deleting passages that needed changed. If I made a mistake, it was either Wite-Out, the correction cartridge (only Smith-Corona fans will know what that means) or Wite-Out tape. I thought that was the greatest invention ever. To me, they could have closed the Patent Office once Wite-Out tape appeared. Often times, when you finished a page and noticed too many errors, you just rewrote the entire page. Computers and printers make the actual writing, editing, and printing functions so much easier.

When it comes to research, much of what you need to find is available immediately on the internet. I used to have to go to a library to review journals, call or send letters to trade associations, subscribe to magazines connected to a subject I needed to learn about, or call offices and try to arrange an interview with a person who had knowledge about a subject I needed to learn. Now, one can Google around the internet and find much—if not most—of what they need to when putting together an outline.

The foe part of writing comes from too much technology. Crushed attention spans are a byproduct. A person who writes has to find a way to "refrain their brain" from too much technology and thinking about too many subjects at the same time. I realized that once my creative soul and focused brainstorming helped me write an outline, I had to let whatever project I was on take up more space in my brain. I had to figure out how to put other ideas onto the back burner so I could concentrate on what I needed to write.

One of the avenues I've pursued is Transcendental Meditation (TM). I'm a student. At the time of this writing, I'm not a good student. I do, however, appreciate the ability of TM to slow my brain, allow my creative soul to be more productive and rid my brain of fatigue and stress. I will discuss my interest in TM later but, for now, I am striving to be a better student and take advantage of the benefits TM offers.

People who live their life like a writer are inquisitive and open minded. They are interested in many, many subjects, events and people. But they are intensely interested in a select few subjects. And these are what they tend to write about. These few are the "road of excess".

CHAPTER THREE

The Right Time to Write is Right Now

Now that your brain has been trained to think like a writer—let's write. You know that book you've been talking about for 22 years? Get started on it. That idea you have for a screenplay? What are you waiting for? That experience that happened to you many years ago? Might be perfect for an article to be submitted to a magazine or newspaper. That letter you owe to your former friend, lover or family member? Get it written and get it off your "to do" list.

Please note: the objectivity and creative thinking that you need to write will not come immediately or easily, but you have to live on that road every day (another good use of the "road of excess"). The road of objectivity and creative thinking is the only one that will get you to the palace of cathartic and ancillary benefits.

<u>"Capture the Creativity"</u>

Even though movies and television shows are written by talented writers, they do not do justice when writing a scene about writing. How many shows and movies have you seen where the actor or actress is at a keyboard writing away, an ashtray full of cigarette butts close by, a garbage can with crumpled up papers around it? That's not writing. Most of the process of writing takes place away from your typewriter or keyboard. You have your moment of inception and you have an idea. You put that idea into your subconscious and go about your daily life. Another idea connected to the first and then another idea connects the two. You are developing a premise. Your creativity is at work. Even at this stage, it is important to "capture the creativity". When I started to write I carried around a small 3 x 5 notebook (the type with the spiral binding at the top). Any ideas for the project I was working on or future projects went into that book. It was on the nightstand next to me as I slept. Napkins, scraps of paper, margins of the newspaper were also called into action. When I got a cell phone, I started sending texts to myself containing project ideas or items I needed to research. As time evolved, I graduated to 4 x 6 notecards. I work off of two desks and a stack of 4 x 6 cards is at each desk. Story ideas, outline ideas for books, ideas that will enhance the classes I teach, and ideas for my investment practice find their way onto these cards.

When I started to write—after becoming an expert on writing cover letters that went largely unread—the format I chose (or chose me) was screenwriting. There is nothing more difficult to write than a motion picture screenplay (OK, an opera would be far more difficult, but that's for a book somebody else can write). A screenplay is the most difficult writing format because it has a pre-determined length of 100 – 120 pages in proper screenplay format. A novel can be less than 100 pages (a "novella") or an extensive saga (hardback version of Ayn Rand's *The Fountainhead* is 753 pages).

The writer of a screenplay can't tell their story using the first person or the third person. If the first 20 – 25 pages of a script aren't structured properly (characters introduced, a reason to like or dislike those characters, their situations (conflicts), and subplots started) you've lost the "screenplay war." First 25 pages are almost like their own screenplay; if not started correctly, there is no way you can recover in the remaining 80 – 90 pages. The format is unique to itself. A typical screenplay page has more white than printed words. Most difficult format to write, without a doubt.

But it's that difficulty that will help you as you increase and advance with your writing.

I advise you to start—or add to—your writing life by writing a screenplay. If you can master the 26 different items a screenwriter must think about, move your premise to a story, then an outline, than a completed script, that experience will make the process of writing your book, article, essay, love letter, business plan, important email, etc., just a tad easier. (One of the documents used in my writing class is "Thinking Like a Screenwriter". It lists those 26 items and provides examples of specific scenes in specific movies that coincide).

Premise to Story to Outline to Screenplay

The Premise to Story to Outline concept is how you should write anything—even if it is not going to be a screenplay but a 900-word piece for the local newspaper or an important email. This is how you write while maintaining your family, work and other commitments.

The Writing Process

When you have done the objective and creative thinking that goes into all writing projects and written and rewritten your outline many times, you are ready to write. Here is a list of how to survive and thrive in the process.

Keep a Strict Writing Schedule

You need to set aside certain days and times for your writing and defend those times.

Let's say you'll be a weekend writer. During the week, you take care of your business and other responsibilities. You may work on your outline, you may give thought to the parts of your outline you will be addressing soon, and you may be working on other projects. But the actual writing is saved for the weekend. There are a few advantages to doing this. If you carve out the same days and times to work on projects, and you stick to that schedule for 5 to 7 weeks, your scheduled time will become a habit. I once read that Eric Clapton didn't touch a guitar on the days he was to perform. He trusted his roadies to tune his guitars. The first time he touched a guitar on performance day was when he walked onto the stage and it was handed to him. It's an exciting feeling during the week knowing that come Saturday and Sunday (or Wednesday and Thursday nights) you will be writing.

I know a doctor who has a demanding daily schedule. He also happens to be a prolific writer. His writing time is daily from 5 a.m. to 7 a.m. When I start a project, I am a weekend writer. As I progress with the project, I tend to add one day during the week. I'm a slow writer and I need that extra day to move the process along once it's underway.

Energy Level

One of the advantages to having a finite schedule to write is it helps preserve your energy level. By thinking about the project during the week (or afternoon and early evening in the case of the doctor) you develop a certain energy in the day or time leading up to your writing. Make no mistake about it: writing is physically and mentally fatiguing. I've done physical labor at different times in my life. I've gone on 100-mile bicycle rides and done 2-mile swims. I've also done a tremendous amount of writing. No contest. Writing is more tiring than physical labor and strenuous exercise.

Staying in Good Physical and Mental Condition

This book deals with your physical and mental health in other sections. But here is an important overlapping benefit. To write, you have to be physically able to handle the fatigue. Your mind needs to be stress-free; you can't be like a younger version of me—thinking my hangovers would make me write better. While I still do drink beer and Riesling wine, I do it in moderation and certainly not to excess as in my "ballroom" days. I also don't do it before or during a writing session. *An upcoming chapter discusses alcohol.*

Finish a Writing Day Knowing Where The Next Writing Day Starts

This is one of life's little pleasures. Knowing the starting point of the next writing session makes life so much sweeter. It also makes the time between writing sessions so much more relaxing. The idea of "I'm stuck!" should really be resolved during the outline process.

Take Advantage of "The Sponge"

If you have trained your brain correctly when you are in the outline or writing stage, you will be able to utilize "The Sponge". The Sponge means you have loaded your subconscious with the variables of your story, or book subject, or article and your creativity will on fire. You really need this during the outline process. Done right, it will carry over into the writing process.

Writer's Block (WB)

If you write, you will have writer's block. On occasion. But the time to have it is during the outline phase. This is where your "focused creativity" can solve problems before they develop in the writing phase. I developed a theory about the reason for WB—we undertake a writing project that is so damn important to us that instead of our subconscious helping us with creativity, that same subconscious is telling us that we aren't smart enough or talented enough to find the words equal to the importance of the project. End result is one gets blocked.

The idea of limiting writing days limits the chance of WB. If you're spending the week living your life thinking about the upcoming writing session, it will help you when you sit down to write.

All writers will tell you, one of the things you should do when WB comes to call is to put "something—anything—down on paper." It is easier to clean up something you've written than to write something when you have a case of WB. There will be times when you are going to have to "suck it up and tough it out" and commit something to paper. A popular saying among writers is "You can't edit a blank page."

If you are really stuck, it is wise to recheck your outline. Maybe the problem is not where you are stuck but in the outline phase. You should also go to the beginning and read what you've written to the point where WB set in. You may have fresh eyes by this point. When you read up to the point where you're stuck, you may break the block by figuring "where to" next. You can also work on other stories, outlines, ideas or research for other projects if you develop a case of WB.

There is a romantic connotation to Writer's Block. Some use it as an excuse to drink alcohol (nobody ever has Alcohol Block) or abandon a project. I'm sure many would-be writers have sat on a bar stool telling the young lovely next to them that they're a writer currently suffering from Writer's Block ("...and how about I buy us some drinks?"). I can share that experience. I know people who claimed Writer's Block before they wrote anything. It doesn't work that way. You must write in order to have Writer's Block.

The Speed of Your Project

Over the years, I've taught my writing class in different ways to different people. People who inquire about the class—but never end up taking it—tend to ask, "How long will it take to write a book?" "How long will it take to write a screenplay?" Those people don't want to commit the time and effort involved. Writing is not easy. But others have done it and you can too—if you follow the "Train Your Brain" and "Refrain Your Brain" techniques.

During a writing project, if your project is going too fast, there's probably something wrong. You probably haven't yet acquired the objectivity needed to write. Your book or screenplay is too simplistic. You may not have done the research needed to make certain words yours. The first screenplay I wrote was titled *Last of the*

Ninth. The story was about the steel mill in the South Side of Pittsburgh and the local union steward's family. The main character was the steward's son who graduates from high school at the outset of the story. I wrote about working in a steel mill. How many times had I been in a mill? Zero. What did I know about working in a steel mill? Absolutely nothing. I just wrote what I thought steel mills, union halls, and the threat of the company closing a mill down would be like. And I wrote it in a matter of a few weeks.

Knowing what I know now, there is no way I should have written that script. But my youthful naivety got in the way and I did write it. And it served two purposes: it enabled me to get some "writing garbage" out of my system, and it resulted in an agent from the William Morris Agency sending me a just-produced script (for the film *True Confessions*) so I could learn the proper format.

Rewriting

Many beginning writers write something and think it's good—for no other reason than they wrote it. I thought my first few projects were good because they were written by me. I had not yet developed the objectivity I now have. You're probably going to guess this next sentence: for any project, the rewriting comes during the outline phase. If you write a screenplay, for example, and after the first draft you decide you need to go in and delete characters, compile others, add a subplot, or change the ending, your mistakes were made when you were thinking of the story and when you were writing your outline. If done right, the rewrite process should be about cleaning up typos, fixing awkward language, deleting needless words, and making unclear passages cleaner and clearer.

Technology and Writing

As discussed in the previous chapter, technology is the writer's friend—but has the potential to be the writer's enemy. Your computer's word processing program makes it so much easier to write and edit. The quick access to research sources via the internet is a blessing but the same quick access to videos, streaming services, news, and email accounts offer quick routes away from writing. To write, you need to have the ability to give your creative soul the proper room to work—and that means at times to be away from technology. I love to go for three-hour bicycle rides without my smartphone. I carry a flip phone for emergencies. I have come to appreciate the feeling of returning from my bike ride wondering "Who called?" "What interesting emails did I get while I was gone?"

When I started writing screenplays, I had to set the tabs on the Smith-Corona electric typewriter. The last screenplay I wrote, *Under a Cuban Sky*, was written using Fade In screenwriting software. The tabs were set for me! When I started writing a location or character name that had been written before, the program recognized this and entered the location or name. Screenwriting software is this generation's Wite-Out. Once finished, instead of having to print copies of the screenplay, the script can be sent in a PDF format to interested parties or can be entered into the most prestigious screenwriting contest, the Nicholl Fellowship.

Technology makes it so much easier to present your final product. This is most evident with Amazon's KDP (Kindle Direct Publishing) platform. Instead of writing a manuscript and sending inquiry letters to literary agents with a summary of your work asking if they would read it, you can self-publish your book using KDP. The platform allows you to list a book for sale in both POD (Print on Demand) and eBook. The buyer has the choice. The process requires a well-edited manuscript, a layout for the book, and a cover page including the front cover, the spine, and the back cover. Without having to deal with agents telling you how busy they are, or "publishing consultants" who will take your money and provide little value in return, you can present a professional-looking, well-written, well-edited book on Amazon.

To repeat: technology is the writer's friend but has the potential to become the writer's enemy. Know the power of technology but understand the potential of technology to limit your creativity. Live your writer's life accordingly.

Two final thoughts for this chapter:

Before she was my client, a woman I deal with got together with her sisters and produced a 35-page booklet about their father's experiences in WWII. The father was in the Army and took part in "Operation Market Garden". In September of 1944, the Allies thought they could parachute into the Netherlands and push the German Army over the Rhine River back into Germany. But the

Germans were still strong in the city of Arnhem and the offensive failed. My client's father earned the nickname "Lucky" because every patrol he went on, something happened to one of his fellow soldiers but nothing happened to him. There was a memorable story of Lucky and two GI's behind a tall manure pile in a field. A sniper was shooting the occasional shot into the pile. Lucky told his crew that after dark they would crawl away on their bellies. The other two soldiers thought they were safe from the sniper right where they were. Lucky's attempt to persuade them failed. The next day, Lucky returned to the manure pile and found two dead U.S. soldiers. That family has that booklet forever. Grandchildren and great grandchildren will know exactly what happened to their ancestor in WWII. You can be the one that writes your story or your family's story. Don't be like my aunt waiting for a clean house in order to write. Start the process now.

The second greatest novel I've read is *Invisible Man* (1952) by Ralph Ellison. Fifteen years after it was published, the follow-up manuscript Ellison was working on was destroyed in a house fire. There was no computer file or external hard drive to turn to. Ellison didn't take the 300+ pages to the local copy shop to make a copy in case of a fire—because there probably was no local copy shop at the time. Ellison died without rewriting his second novel (although his literary executor did piece together a book credited to Ellison five years after his death). Imagine if Ralph Ellison had access to even the most basic computer. That manuscript could have been saved in a few different ways. I think about this manuscript as I'm writing it compared to the book you are now reading. If it was suddenly taken away from me, I couldn't go back and restart it. As soon as I finish writing this sentence, I'm going to back up to my external hard drive.

CHAPTER FOUR

How do you spend your days?
Second most important chapter in this book

There are three chapters in this book that put me at risk of losing readers. This is the first of the three. If finances aren't in the top three of most important factors in being old and your physical appearance isn't in the top five, the chapter on living your life like a writer plus this chapter make for an incredible one-two combo.

I'm writing this book for people who are in their 20s, 30s and 40s, plus for people who are older and still in the workforce and for people who have left the workforce. I'm also writing it for myself. As I was giving thought to this chapter, I realized it—and the entire book—will be a cathartic experience for me.

Ron Morris (1949–2012) was a Pittsburgh-born and raised businessman who became The American Entrepreneur. He sold a business for a tremendous sum in 1999, became the Professor of Entrepreneurship at Duquesne University, and started a radio program. The show dealt with all issues surrounding starting, operating, and selling businesses. I was a big fan and a regular listener to the program. Ron started out only on Saturday mornings but expanded to a Monday through Saturday schedule. There was a question Ron asked often during his show and a comment he made an equal number of times. Both have stuck with me.

"How do you spend your days?" was the question. The comment was the idea of "trading your hours for dollars".

The question dealt with the age-old problem of working in a job that you didn't care for, where you were woefully underemployed, or wasn't providing you with a sense of achievement or accomplishment. The purpose of Ron's show was to motivate people in limited opportunity jobs to become entrepreneurs. The show—and the message—wasn't for everybody. But I certainly got the message loud and clear.

The comment of "trading hours for dollars" also resonated with me. I have had various jobs where I traded hours for dollars even though that wasn't what I really wanted to do. And those "hour-trading" jobs tended to have me carrying things: cement and swimming pool panels, cases of beer and half barrels of the same, and conduit of various sizes for electrical construction projects. My father traded hours for dollars because he had to. He had a family (it wasn't until the last few months of his life that he shared his young man entrepreneurial ambitions with me). I know many talented construction craftsmen who trade their hours for dollars. Their skill level and ability to contribute to construction projects enable them to earn a sizable hourly wage plus a valuable benefit package. When I worked as a laborer on the construction crew, I made $28 per hour, and I was always the lowest paid individual on every job. The "real" electricians made $54 per hour with their benefit package.

I am going to use my experiences and my objective observations to share why I realized it is vitally important to do your best to spend your days in a productive, fulfilling way. I am still active in business and I have no idea what it's like to retire and collect a pension and Social Security. My only insight into what it's like to be out of the work world comes from my dealings with clients and others. Regardless of your situation, it is important to go into each day with a plan. If you go into a day with no plan, your impulse control will go into the "off" position and you'll find yourself bouncing from one thing to another, eating more than you need to, and getting involved in unhealthy pursuits. That first beer tends to happen earlier and earlier in the afternoon to people with no plan. If you have no plan, you will not be rewarded at the end of the day with restful sleep but "stutter sleep" which will do nothing but give you a bad head start for the next "plan-less" day.

Before I list my experiences, I want to share a memory. When I was doing construction work, every so often there would be a Friday afternoon ceremony for a retiring carpenter or plumber. Fellow would be in his 60s, impressive tool belt over his shoulder, having the honor of spending his last day on the job. The ceremony wouldn't last long, a few people would speak to honor their co-worker, and only on a few of the occasions I witnessed were there cans of beer passed around. But the one constant was that the honoree "looked" like he was ready to go. The young man benefits from the physicality of construction work with a lean but muscular body. But after doing it for 40 years, the lean look turns into a slightly stooped back and a paunchy stomach. There are untold lingering injuries and pain from a body part or two. That hard-earned, well deserved pension was about to start paying. I remember thinking: "these are the types of jobs you want to retire from." Tough physical labor under less than ideal weather conditions with a variety of personalities on the sites with you. My main memory of my limited time in the trade: each 8-hour day was like an eternity for me. My co-workers appeared to enjoy the work and talked about hunting, trucks, tools, and the local NFL team. They loved the job because they had the aptitude for it. My aptitude was in other directions.

When I got my job in the real estate development industry, one of my first assignments was to help set up a savings bank in Tampa, Florida. While I was doing that, I was working on real estate projects. I was also researching investment issues, other industries and the home building climate in certain cities. Two months after starting to work, I was sent to Puerto Rico and other Caribbean islands. After battling unemployment for an extended period, I had a unique job. I had different responsibilities, dealt with a wide range of individuals and was able to obtain a "real world" education in a short period of time. Every day was something new. On Sunday afternoon, I was excited for the week to start. What was I going to learn? Who was I going to meet? My week was almost seamless. I was as happy on Monday as I was on Friday. As I was employed by an entity that invested in—and built—real estate projects and was starting a bank, I obtained insight from working both sides of the fence.

A few years into this cool job, my employer asked me to move to Florida and work at the bank full-time. Now, I enjoyed going to Tampa for a week or two, staying at the Hyatt Hotel with the swimming pool on the rooftop and loved the Florida nightlife. But live there? No way. No interest in living in Florida. Plus, I had other projects I wanted to explore and was writing longer, more detailed pieces. My employer and I made an arrangement where I would continue doing contract business research work for him.

Cut forward to a few years later. I had obtained my investment license, received the first of two grants from the PA Council on the Arts and had gotten in—and out—of the satellite television business. I was given the chance to come back to work for my previous employer.

The second tour of duty was not like the first. The job changed and I had changed. Ambition had gotten the better of me. I was doing one focused thing in the real estate business and I was woefully underemployed. Days dragged by. I was not getting the same feeling of creation and achievement as I had been previously. On Sunday afternoon, instead of looking toward the challenges of a new week, I would get a sick feeling in the pit of my stomach. "I got to go through five days before another weekend," was my thought. Not a healthy thought. I'm certain I engaged in unhealthy behavior at night to match the unhealthy way I was spending my days.

It took a long time, with many false starts and figuring out how to get over the wall, but I slowly carved out a life where I spend the majority of my days in productive, creative, fulfilling, healthy ways. I can do what I love to do: research into the areas I have passion for and find ways to convey what I've learned to clients, potential clients and others. What helped me to get to that position was my writing ability and the ancillary benefits I've obtained from writing. In outlining this chapter for the book, I came to a life-affirming conclusion. I have a creative soul and an ambitious spirit. I get up each day thinking about what I can create, achieve, and accomplish. Most days include moments of insight, creation, meditation, physical activity and the "advancing of my cause" (my business ventures and outside activities I'm involved in). I've come a long way from the Sunday afternoons with the horrible stomach ache and facing another week of underemployment—and it all happened when I recognized and saluted my creative soul.

Notice I used the word "most". While I would not trade my creativity and ambition, and while I wouldn't detour from doing the things I want to do, there are those on the other side of the table who aren't interested in creating, achieving, and accomplishing. It makes for a challenge when dealing with people who are just playing out the string. And this is a perfect spot to reintroduce the cathartic aspects of writing. Of the various people I must deal with, there are far too many who feel the need to tell me how busy they are. The writing of "Busy Nation" pays dividends to me three years after I wrote it and it was published.

If you have been blessed with a creative soul, or acquire one through life experiences, this is even more reason for you to "train your brain" to think like a writer and to live your life the way a writer does.

If you're a younger person with many days ahead of you, and you're getting that Sunday afternoon awful feeling in your stomach, you need to do what you need to do to put yourself in a position to spend your days in a more productive, healthier way.

I deal with a number of retired individuals. Their finances are solid. I can categorize them in three ways. (1) those who retired and took to "flying their couch" and worrying about what to make for dinner, (2) those who have full schedules thanks to charity work, consultancy with non-profits, time with children's families and grandchildren, (3) those whose physical and mental health issues have moved them from one of the other two categories.

I would tell young and old to give thought as to how their days are being spent, and to take steps to make their days happier, healthier and more productive. I would also tell all ages to reframe a quote from Chapter One. That quote, "Don't live the same year 80 times and call it a life," can be rewritten as "Don't live the same day 365 times and call it a year."

Joe Namath Returns

When I think of how people spend their days, I think of people like Joe Namath. He was 26 years old when he ran off the field with his index finger raised to the sky (again, the only person who should be allowed to do so) after winning Super Bowl III. When accomplishing something so great at such a young age, where do you go from there? How many athletes had their best day or days in their chosen sport before the age of 25? How many performers acted in or wrote a well-received movie at a young age? How many musicians have a great album (to younger readers: a collection of songs, sometimes with a common theme, was an album) before their 30s? When you do something that puts you on the top, or near the top of your profession at such a young age, where do you go next? It has to be challenging to have great success so young and then go on with the minutiae of life. I've read Namath's book and have seen him interviewed. He's literate, has great memory recall and his cognitive function seems to be spot on. He credits this to 100+ trips to the hyperbaric chamber to resume blood flow to areas in his brain affected by numerous concussions from playing football. Maybe the alcohol issues Namath shared with the world were fueled by having great success at such a young age. Joe now appears to be spending his days in a healthy, productive way. But how many people who had success young let their laurels get in the way of a productive life?

Early laurels—and the accompanying trappings of success—have waylaid many successful recording artists. But there are others who were able to digest early success and stay creative and "stay in the game." I have an eclectic taste in music and listen to music of all genres. I still listen to the groups (Isley Brothers, Grand Funk Railroad, Average White Band) whose albums I inherited from my older brother. Some of the groups that I grew up on and influenced me are still active in their trade. When somebody tells me they can't believe the Rolling Stones or The Who are still touring, I tell them two things: (1) If that's what you do, that's what you're going to do. If going on a stage and singing songs written fifty years ago is what gives you a sense of purpose, then more power to you. (2) As a person who writes and points to a stronger memory as one of the many ancillary benefits of writing, I appreciate 70+ year old rockers still plying their trade. I know that the songs they've written, the ones they are thinking about writing and the lyrics they have to remember (OK, so there's a teleprompter onstage) have led to strong memories, stable levels of cognitive function and executive function and less cases of dementia. So, you can guess the next line: another reason to write and train your brain to think like a writer.

One of my favorite Bruce Springsteen quotes is, "The older you get, the more it means." As I was outlining this book and specifically this chapter, I thought of that quote many times. I think of it in different aspects that I want to share in closing this chapter.

When I got my job in the real estate development industry after a long bout of unemployment, people asked me how I was able to get such an interesting job. I told them about the epiphany I had while working on the swimming pool job in Bethel Park. I told them it was at that moment I realized the human resources people I was sending resumes to were just playing out the string. There wasn't an ounce of ambition among the lot and their futures were behind them. That last tag line became this quote, "Never let your future get behind you." No matter your age, and as long as you have your mental faculties, that quote holds true. Be looking to do something—write, paint, help a non-profit or charity, or share your experiences and insights with your family and others. Just don't let your future get behind you—or take a job in HR.

There are three essays on my website grouped together as "The Trinity". The subjects are Aptitude, Persistence, and Ambition. The Ambition essay detailed my long-ago goal to be a cameraman working for a local TV station. "What a great gig," I thought with my 20-year-old brain. I would leave the station early in the morning with the star reporter in the station van. People would let us into traffic because they knew we were on important assignments and we were in the van of their favorite station. We would capture the list of assignments from the assignment editor (I could never dream of having that lofty position) and then rush back to the station where my superb editing skills would craft stories for that evening's news. When a story that I filmed and edited aired on the six o'clock news, I would be sitting in a downtown bar. A pretty secretary who stopped in for happy hour drinks would be sitting a few bar stools away. When I would tell her that I was the cameraman and editor of the story she just watched, she would certainly pick up her drink and slide closer to me. And, if by some small chance, she wasn't there for the six o'clock news, she certainly would be there for the 11 o'clock version. That, at one time, was my ambition. As my world vision opened and my 20-year-old brain became a 30-year-old brain, I realized how limited that ambition is. That may be a cool job—for about three days. Then it would be worse than carrying heavy conduit into buildings under construction. When people complain to me about being too busy, I tell them they shouldn't be watching the local news. Every 30 minute newscast is 2 minutes of station promos, 8 minutes of commercials, 5 minutes of sports, 4 minutes of weather, 1 minute of banter between the anchors and 10 minutes of news that can be obtained in 1 minute on the internet *(then I email them "Busy Nation")*.

Ambition is a double-edged sword. I wasn't really an ambitious person coming up. After college, I just wanted to get a 9-5 job with a downtown corporation, play third base on the company softball team and stop in at Froggy's Pub for Friday happy hour. It was my bout with unemployment—even more than my spinal surgery—that gave me ambition. I had no other choice than to be ambitious. When I started to write complete screenplays and received some positive feedback, the feeling of creation I received provided inherent satisfaction and the desire to create more things. But my story is not everybody's and I respect that.

In *Cut Your Calories…Now!!* I referenced an article published in June of 2009 in *The Economist*. This is one of my favorite magazines. It is published in England and provides insight into American business and life that domestic publications don't. The article in question was titled "Mild and bitter: The evolutionary origin of depression." The author of the piece cited research done by University of Michigan psychologist Randolph Neese. Dr. Neese's observation is that a percentage of the population suffers from "low mood". According to Neese, low mood is a protective device used to shield some of us from psychological damage by "pursuing unreachable goals". In the same way mild pain caused by an activity prevents you from continuing that activity and causing more pain, those with low mood realize their goals and ambitions are too lofty and halt the pursuit of those dreams in order to prevent "mind damage" (my paraphrased term). The article was referenced in a book about nutrition, as some people whose ambitions and goals aren't met may overeat and consume calorie-dense alcohol to excess. To these people, ambition may be unhealthy from both a physical and a mental standpoint.

I respect the individuals Dr. Neese was writing about. I respect the fact they must spend their days in jobs that don't carry the baggage of entrepreneurial pursuits that go unfulfilled or artistic endeavors that nobody sees, reads, or listens to. I do not respect, however, those people who reside in Busy Nation and only get a feeling of creation by doing what they can to prevent others from actually creating.

There was a time when I did something or went somewhere because I thought it was the "thing to do". There were various business events or social gatherings I attended. More times than not, I realized after the event it wasn't a good use of my time, I wasn't a better person for having attended and the time spent didn't help me to advance any of my causes. As I got older, I got wiser with my time. It's important in concluding a chapter titled *"How do you spend your days?"* to make sure you don't steal or waste anybody's time—

most importantly your own. There is a quote I think about often: "The real thief steals your time, not your money."

You can always get your money back, but you can never get your time back.

How To Be Old

CHAPTER FIVE

The way you look tonight*
...and in the daytime!
cool 1964 song by Frank Sinatra

A few years ago, I was at a meeting. A young man who worked in the office—whose name happened to be Ken—and I were talking about movies and actresses. I told him I always thought Kim Novak was one of the most beautiful women ever. He was not familiar. I asked him to Google her name. Up popped a photo of Kim Novak—85 years old and after bad plastic surgery. "No, no," I said. You have to see her when she was younger. Put the title *Picnic* after her name." Ken did so and we were looking at Kim in a still photo from the movie that I think captures her beauty the best. He acknowledged she was a gorgeous woman but then he said something I never forgot and have repeated many times: "Father Time is undefeated." *(I certainly am not going to bet against him!)*

This chapter is divided into two sections: Physical Appearance and Physical Activity. The next chapter is also two sections: Nutrition and the Supplement Industry. Both chapters will use my experience and writings on the subjects and will be presented for all ages.

PART ONE

Physical Appearance

Physical appearance doesn't crack the top five in order of importance but deserves a lot of attention. Its contribution to this section will focus on how we can deal with the changes in our physical appearance—even though many of us would like to forget the age-old adage, "The only thing constant is change." Physical Activity will encompass increasing and incorporating more varied physical activity into our lives. The section will discuss and detail "working out," gym behavior, dealing with personal trainers, and ways to avoid "exercise bulimia" (not my term; coined by somebody much smarter than me).

I am dedicating this chapter to the woman introduced in Chapter One who was under the mistaken impression that aging is all about your appearance *(and here's to hoping she found that one guy who thought she looked good at 54 years of age).*

As I write this, Kim Novak is still alive. You may be reading this after she (and others mentioned in the book) have "Gone to Glory". So, for now I'll use the present tense. I wonder what Kim Novak thinks when she wakes up in the morning and sees her image in the mirror. Does she think, "I was once one of the most beautiful women in the world...and look at me now!" Or does she think, "Hey, I'm looking pretty, pretty good today!" And then goes on about her day.

I don't know what the answer is but I do know this: hundreds of millions of ad dollars are spent each year in an attempt to get you to spend part of your money on treatments, techniques and devices to make you look younger. Skin peels and dermabrasions, nose jobs, chin implants, breast implants, butt and calf implants (they actually do those), liposuction, dental veneers, teeth whitening, hair transplants, tummy tucks, ear tucks and so on. The weight loss and fitness industries will be addressed separately. And while these items may help you feel good about yourself—in addition to generating revenue for cosmetic surgeons and dentists and other providers—the "Father Time" lesson is this: you are going to look different as you age. Your skin tone and texture will change, your muscle mass will decrease (causing a decline in your RMR—resting metabolic rate), you will lose height due to a decline in your "bone bank" which includes your spinal column, your hair may thin, turn grey, fall out, recede—or all of the above or some of the above.

Thanks to the motion picture camera and a hundred plus ways to watch movies, there are many Kim Novak-like situations. One of my favorite actors was William Holden. When I first went to Thailand, I was determined to travel to the River Kwai. *The Bridge on the River Kwai* starring Holden had a major influence on me (of course, when I got there I found out Americans weren't there but a major U.S. star was needed for the movie). *Sunset Boulevard* is a must see for anybody interested in motion pictures. My favorite World War II movie, hands down, is *Stalag 17*, which won Holden the Academy Award for Best Actor. There is no better "Ah ha!" moment in movies than when Holden's character uncovers Peter Graves' character as the barracks spy. He was in *Picnic* with Ms. Novak. That guy won the Genetic Lottery. He couldn't have been more handsome. But he was a smoker and over consumed alcohol. If you watch his later movies, his looks were leaving in a hurry. He developed the voice of a heavy drinker and smoker. The movie *Network* came out in 1976. Holden played Max Schumacher, the craggy, gin-guzzling old-time newsman. And he was craggy. I watched the movie a few years ago and wondered how old Holden was when he made the film. I was stunned to find out that wrinkled, gravel-voiced Bill Holden was 58 years of age. I was the same age. (Holden died tragically; passed out from drinking, hit his head on an end table and bled out. He was 63.)

My major contribution to this section of the chapter came a few years ago when I wrote an essay about my hair. Now, that sentence may read funny to you. A guy writing a tribute to his follicles? What the...? But it was something that had been on my mind (pun intended) for a long time. Even in my twenties, I wondered what would happen to my hair in the years ahead (pun not intended). As I saw friends lose their hair, have it turn different shades of gray or develop bigger foreheads, I couldn't help but wonder what would happen to my hair. The essay, titled "September of My Hair" (with credit to Sinatra's song *September of My Years*) has ended up being one of the most impactful and cathartic things I've written—even if the impact and catharsis has been measured only by me. The piece (again, with the unintended pun) is shared with you below.

SEPTEMBER OF MY HAIR
(w/ credit to Frank Sinatra's "September of My Years")

As difficult as it is to admit, I am in the September of my years. It's not the end of the month or the middle; it's more like the Labor Day Weekend. But it is here. And this is as good a time as any to address an important part of my life: my hair. (Note to editor: no quotation marks around part, please)

I had great hair as a kid. In the endless summers of youth, my light brown hair turned even lighter with all the sun I consumed by being outside for hours and hours. My mother once told me if summer lasted one more month, I would end up with blonde hair.

My teenage years were another matter. My hair grew out sideways and not straight. The night before the ninth grade yearbook photo was to be taken, my mother commented that she didn't want my photo taken with my hair looking the way it did. My father cut the hair of my two brothers and me on occasion and this was one of the occasions he chose to give me a trim. I'm sure my mother would have prevented him from doing so if she knew exactly how many Old Milwaukees he drank before taking scissors to her middle son. It wasn't the picture with the semi-bowl cut I remember; it's the nickname Coach Thompson gave me. "Pigman." It's wrong when a teacher and athletic coach provides mean-spirited nicknames for the students. That's the job of the other students.

There was a thankfully short period of time when I adopted the part down the middle style. Because my hair didn't grow straight, this didn't look so good. I refer to this as my "stoner" period.

Things started happening when the "straight back" style was adopted. My hair had the perfect length and curl for this look. Many compliments, and some girlfriends, came my way. Some thought I adopted this style because I wanted to appear tougher than I was. The simple truth is that I suffered from the scourge of youth— acne—and my blotchy face, coupled with my broken nose from tenth grade football, made it difficult for me to look in mirrors. I wanted a style that required a minimum amount of time looking at myself. The James Dean-inspired "do" served the purpose.

As I was finishing my business studies in college, I needed a more respectable cut. The band Duran Duran was popular at the time. The lead singer, Simon LeBon, had cool hair. Long on the sides with a part left of center. I copied it the best I could and it worked. One of the few photographs of myself that I like is my college yearbook photo.

Once out of college and some years in my profession, I was able to go to the straight back style. I took this style in high school to avoid looking at my acne. I "readopted" it because I didn't like looking at the uninvited grey hair—not quite gray and not quite white—that had crashed the party and took up residence on the sides of my head.

One of my friends once said, "Every five years or so Mother Nature gives you a new hair style--whether you want one or not." My last new hair style was a combination George Clooney/Steve

McQueen cut. It worked well—for five years. It may be time for a change soon.

What's the future hold for me and my hair? More recession? A bigger forehead? A bald spot? The "Mel Cooley" look? (younger readers may have to Google that one). Will the uninvited grey take over the whole neighborhood?

I've lost the thickness and curl that caught much female attention over the years. That's the bad news. The good news: the top-secret treatment I now use to diffuse the chlorine my hair is exposed to in the YMCA pool five times per week seems to be working. I would share the secret here but then it would no longer be top secret.

It is a good thing I never relied on my physical appearance to get by in this life. I obtained an education above my level of intelligence and I developed unique outside interests. I traveled. I explored. I created. I paid as much attention to keeping my body in shape as I did expanding my mind.

And I gained experiences, insights, and abilities I never imagined I would possess when I—and my hair—were much younger. One of those abilities—the ability to write—is a skill not to be traded for anything—even for a Simon LeBon haircut. *(Note to reader: the anti-chlorine secret referred to in the essay is coconut oil.)*

The point to what you just read is at an early age I accepted things would happen to my hair. Unlike many people I've encountered over the years, I didn't (couldn't) trade on my looks. I got an education I didn't deserve, turned my ambition toward creative causes, developed outside interests, wrote, and traveled. I prepared myself for whatever came my way, hairwise.

There is a funny story to the genesis of the essay. I have two clients who own art galleries. One of the galleries represents new and established artists. A fellow who played college and professional football became an artist. When you see his work you are immediately aware of his talent. He would come by the gallery on occasion looking for representation. That gallery owner did not wish to represent him. One day when he came to the gallery to show some paintings, he and I met. When he learned of my experiences seeing the paintings of Johannes Vermeer, we developed a bond.

We found ourselves in the gallery one Saturday. At the time, I had the inception for the idea that would become the essay you just read. The artist and I started talking about teaching others to create art. I teach a writing class. He wanted to teach painting and was convinced anybody can develop painting skills. I was excited about the tribute to my hair I was going to write. My enthusiasm leaked into our conversation. As I was telling him about my newest idea, I could see the reaction in his eyes. "This guy is going to write about his hair? WTF?" I should share that this gentleman happens to be African-American and has long dreadlocks. He is many years away from having to worry about his hair. I see him from time to time around town. I can't help but think his first thought when he sees me is, "There's that strange guy who wrote about his hair." The cathartic power of that essay, by the way, gets stronger with each passing year.

Kim Novak and Bill Holden are just two examples of celebrities whose aging process (good or bad) has been captured on motion picture film. Marlon Brando received letters from motion picture studios stating that he was losing his looks and needed to stop gaining weight when he was only 35 years old. Errol Flynn, known for playing Robin Hood, Captain Blood and others (as well as for giving us the expression, "In like Flynn") was an amazing looking young man. But drink, drugs, legal issues and three marriages may have voided Flynn's ticket. He looked far beyond 50 when he died at that age.

I wasn't appearing in front of movie cameras during my 20s, 30s and 40s. I do, however, have my photograph on two book covers. The photos are from the years 2002 and 2003, and I'm as happy with the way the covers look today as when they first came out. The books are around my office so I see them on a regular basis. On occasion I share one of the books with visitors. Their reaction is to look at the photos, then look up at me, and ask how old the photos are. Some less diplomatic folks have told me I changed a lot or have asked, "What happened to you?" Nothing happened to me—except life. And life will happen to us all.

As you have more birthdays, you will tend to gain weight, which is a natural progression from a decline in your muscular structure and a slowing down of your cells dividing and replicating. You will lose height due to your spinal column contracting. You will lose collagen and elastin in your skin. You will develop wrinkles around your mouth and eyes. Your face, based on your ticket in the Genetic

Lottery, may become a fat depository. Your hair will undergo changes—based on the ticket you were given (I'm a walking, talking, writing example of this one).

Don't overspend money or time on reversing the changes in your physical appearance. It will be a waste of both resources. Certainly, there is no issue in getting plastic surgery, cosmetic dental work or similar work. But don't use it as an excuse not to develop the other "aging skills" one must have. Don't think that chin implant (usually second most common plastic surgery for men) will bring you happiness, contentment, and a surge in your popularity.

Negative Energy

If "epiphany" is my favorite word in the English language, "aura" is in a close second place. If your aura is negative—if you aren't spending your days in a productive, creative way and if you're walking around with zero objectivity under the false impression that your opinions matter, your physical appearance will be affected. Your negative aura will impact your appearance—even if you won the Genetic Lottery. People are overly concerned about their physical appearance but aren't doing anything to stop the "inside out" from detracting from their "outside in". To the millions of people walking around emitting negative energy, I suggest they return to the chapter on living life like a writer. These people need to develop objectivity and a creative soul. They need to find a point to their existence. Ambition, creativity, and unique outside interests—these are attractive features that add to our appearance.

That One Year

There is one footnote to "life will happen to us all". I had one year where I think the change in my appearance was sped up by life events. It was the year 2008. It was the year the U.S. stock market declined by 38.49%. To remind: I'm an investment advisor. I also got engaged in October of that year. The week after I got engaged, the U.S. stock market declined by 18.19%. My (then) fiancée had been accepted to graduate school in Florida and I was going to have to get an apartment in that state. I was in a constant mode of stress with concern over my clients' money, my investment practice, and the transition to Florida. I could feel the stress hormones circulating in my chest cavity and sleep was only a dream (meaning I wasn't sleeping well). One of my clients uses the expression, "Everybody gets their turn in the barrel." My turn in the barrel was 2008.

I turned the negativity of calendar year 2008 into a positive. One of the few people in the investment industry whose opinion I respect told me, "Ken, you will be remembered for what you do when you don't know what to do." What I did was develop an expertise in negative market investing. I studied the frequency of negative markets and how to structure client portfolios, knowing that negative days, months, and years happen—and how often. This knowledge has helped me going forward. As an advisor, I realized my main function was to make sure my clients—and me—sleep well at night. I may have aged in that one year at a pace equal to three or four years. But it was my time to be in the barrel and I did what I had to do. No complaints from me.

My fourth book, *The Confusing Muse*, is about dating, romance, and relationships. The book will be highlighted in an upcoming chapter. It is being introduced here because there is a chapter on clothes and fashion in the book. It can make you feel better about yourself and more comfortable in all situations. We need to learn which designers make clothes that fit our bodies the best, and purchase clothes that maintain their quality after many wearings and washings. We should be comfortable with the colors we wear. I do not have one piece of brown clothing for this reason: when I graduated from college I only had one suit. It was a brown double-knit polyester suit. I had to wear it over and over while going on job interviews that didn't result in a job. I grew to hate that suit. When I finally found employment I burned that suit (actually threw it away). If there was a Bad Suit Hall of Fame, that brown suit would be a member.

So, we know our physical appearance will change and we have limited control over that process. But we do have some control over our "sartorial splendor" (our attire; how we dress). This is an area where one should invest research time, energy and money to make sure they have a closet filled with clothes that they are comfortable in. And we need to update our closets at least once a year. Give away what you're not wearing or what you're no longer comfortable wearing.

Which brings us to the perfect ending for this section. My cousin came back to Pittsburgh for her 50th high school class reunion. After the event, we talked about how physical appearances change at different rates for different people but that the personalities of some 68-year-olds are disappointingly similar to their 18-year-old selves. Then my cousin shared a quote that I knew would end up in this book, "A person should always dress age appropriate and body-type appropriate." I'll put that quote right up there with the one about Father Time's undefeated record.

PART TWO

Physical Activity

It's less important to think of the concepts of "working out" and "going to the gym" than maintaining consistent and changing physical activity in your life. It's not just helpful—it's vital to maintain physical activity (whatever that activity is) as you age. Here are the main reasons why:

- maintain glycogen storage capability
- increase RMR (resting metabolic rate)
- maintain cardiovascular and lung capacity
- add to your "bone bank" by offsetting naturally occurring bone loss
- maintain proper muscle tone (length) and range of motion
- decreased transit time (time between digestion and elimination)
- production of the "feel good" brain chemicals endorphins & enkephalins

What's my authority to write this section? I once was the leading salesperson of exercise equipment in my city, I have done extensive research into the fitness industry, the metabolic benefits and mistruths of exercise, and I've been a swimmer and cyclist for many years. I'm a believer in yoga and any other physical activity that incorporates using your own body weight for resistance. I am also a fan (for lack of a better term) of the enormous scams connected to the fitness industry. I wrote a highly read article about a beautiful bookstore in my neighborhood that closed and reopened as a fitness facility. That article, "There Used to Be a Bookstore" is among my favorites of the various articles I've had published in the local papers. The relevance of that article is about to be shared with you.

Exercise Bulimia

Of equal importance to having sufficient physical activity in your life is not becoming "exercise bulimic". This is not my term. Somebody with greater insight than I coined the term many years ago. If the percentage of Americans—of all ages—getting enough physical activity to be considered "physically active" is 25% or 33% or whatever, there is an equal (or greater) percentage that is EB (Exercise Bulimic).

EB is characterized by various behaviors. It's two major tenets are being addicted to exercise and a false belief that time in the gym can radically change your body. Addiction to exercise results in too much time spent in the gym, feelings of guilt or anxiety if a workout session is missed, being in that gym when one is injured or sick, and a false understanding that exercise will lead to a body transformation and internal happiness. EB also prevents its sufferers from living a full and complete life. People with EB tend not to start businesses, pursue creative endeavors, and the idea of travel is not on their radar. One of my friends was always afraid to travel to Cuba with me for fear of being detained. The length of the trip to Thailand would have killed him. When I was planning a trip to Rome and Berlin, he swore to me that he would take the trip. He was of Italian descent and wanted to see the country. He started the process of getting a passport but then called me one night with news. The news was that he was not going on the trip because his personal trainer told him he would miss too many workouts (and as I wrote in my article, "…may a 45-pound Universal plate hit me on the head if I'm lying.")

There is no minimum or maximum age for EB. Individuals in their 20s have it and people in their 80s have it. I sometimes think about a young person graduating from college, getting their first job, then an apartment, and then the obligatory gym membership. Are they going to be going to that gym—or another gym—4 to 5 times per week indefinitely? Will they develop EB? Will they not travel, create, volunteer, start a business, all because those worthy endeavors require time away from the gym? The advice for any age is to re-read the short (but important) list of why we need physical activity in our lives. Having physical activity in your life shouldn't detract from that life.

<u>The Gym Life</u>

The economics of the gym industry are odd. A successful gym requires a high percentage of its members to join, provide credit card information, and then not show up. The study I referenced for my article detailed that over 50% of the people with gym memberships don't go to the gym taking money from their bank account on a monthly basis. A facility I once belonged to had 10,000 members. If 5% of us would have showed up during "gym prime time" (after work into early evening M-F) the place would have been so crowded there would have been long waits for machines and it would have been wall-to-wall people. There are people who think having that gym swipe card on their key ring, and having money deducted from a checking account, and then NOT going to the gym are getting some benefit. They're not.

While I do appreciate the people who come into fitness facilities, get their activity in, and leave with minimal socializing, I respect the other end of the spectrum. There are facilities where the "regulars" (usually older men and women) come in at the opening bell and mix their physical activity with socializing. It gives this crew a regiment to follow, social interaction and physical activity. I'm a member of a facility with such regulars and enjoy conversations with most of them. In Chapter One, I shared that I have wasted a lot of time in my life. One of my big-time wasters early on was in a certain fitness facility in the South Hills of Pittsburgh. I started as the guy who went in, lifted what I needed to lift, and left. Over time, I became the social butterfly, talking to others between sets, trying to make time with females in their spandex, etc. I've often stated I wish I could have the time back I spent (wasted) in that place.

<u>FAIS</u>

One of the major issues with EB, and something that needs to be addressed for those engaging in regular activity without suffering from EB, is the concept of Fat Aerobics Instructor Syndrome (FAIS). This acronym (again, not my term) may be offensive to some but the concept behind it is scientific. What it means is that the more one does of a certain activity, the more acclimated that person becomes to it. Their bodies become more efficient. The author of the term made the observation that there were many aerobics instructors who were overweight (most likely in the heyday of bench step aerobics) and coined the term. If somebody's goal is to utilize more calories while exercising, they're defeating their purpose by doing the same routine over and over. One of the biggest marketing ploys the fitness industry uses is the idea that going to a fitness facility (or owning a piece of equipment) will help you "burn" fat. News flash: fat doesn't burn. It oxidizes.

I am a swimmer and a cyclist. I've been doing both for a long time and with a high level of intensity. I am swimming faster and further than ever but it is not a major calorie expenditure for me. It certainly was when I started—given my age (much younger) and my swimming experience (minimal). With cycling, I easily consume more calories during and after a ride than I expend. How does one overcome FAIS? Two ways: by increasing the intensity of what they're doing or, the better way, "fooling" their body. The first has limits. You can only spend so much time in the pool or on a bike. The second way requires you to give up the same routine you've been doing for years and introduce new activity to your body. Been lifting the same amount of weights in the same manner for the last decade? Put the weights down and get in the pool. Have you been walking around a track or on a street for that same decade? Knees permitting, incorporate walking up steps into your routine. Haven't been on a bicycle for a long time? There are now bikes made for all ages and body types. As much as we like our classes, our routines and our instructors (FAIS or not), we need to keep fooling our body to make our physical activity time as efficient and effective as possible.

The Law of Diminishing Returns

Economists use the term "The Law of Diminishing Returns" to describe profit margin. At a certain level of production or sales, a product sees declines in marginal profit after the optimum number is met. After that, the margin starts to decrease with every unit produced or sold. And, contrary to what people afflicted with EB believe, the same applies to exercise. More is not more. Less is more.

How much is "enough?" The Harvard Alumni Study followed 16,936 men who entered Harvard and the University of Pennsylvania between the years 1916 to 1950 (the study was originally titled College Alumni Study). The men were followed to 1978. By that time, 1,413 had died, half from heart disease and one-third from cancer. The men who were active to the point of expending (not burning) 2,000 calories per week had death rates one-quarter to one-third lower than the least active men. The benefits of exercise on all-cause mortality were eliminated at 3,500 calories expended during physical activity per week. While this study is the landmark study in physical activity because it provides a minimum and maximum level of activity, there are a few caveats.

Years after the study was published, I read comments from enrolled participants who shared that they were involved in regular physical activity until a health event (heart attack, cancer diagnosis) sidelined them. That will happen. Regular, non-EB physical activity will not prevent adverse health events. My swimming and previous weightlifting schedule resulted in two torn rotator cuffs. An early morning post-swimming run on the treadmill resulted in a trip to the ER with chest, shoulder, and upper back tightness. A CAT scan revealed no heart issue. A few days after the incident, it was determined that I pulled a muscle in my upper back while on the treadmill. But it could have been a heart issue. Instead of "Why me?" I would have said, "Why not me?" There are many people engaged in sufficient regular activity who get the diagnosis that halts that activity.

Excessive time spent at exercise (EB or not), in addition to being affected by FAIS and The Law of Diminishing Returns, also puts one at increased risk for Repetitive Motion Injuries (RMI). *(Take it from a swimmer and former heavy weightlifter with two surgically-repaired rotator cuffs).*

The Harvard Alumni Study is well-known, well-documented and well-discussed. Aside from the major issue with the study shared above, there is this: it is one of thousands, if not tens of thousands, of studies correlating regular physical activity and decreased mortality, improved mobility, longevity, etc. In spite of all the money being spent on these studies, and all the media attention given when a new study appears, we as a country still have two major issues: (1) not enough adults are getting sufficient physical activity in their schedules and (2) a high percentage of people who have sufficient activity have gone too far and crossed over into becoming Exercise Bulimic. Why haven't all these paid-for studies done anything to correct either issue?

Resistance (and Progressive Resistance) Training

While you shouldn't waste time in gyms and while you better respect the important message behind FAIS, the Law of Diminishing Returns and EB, there is something you SHOULD do: engage in Resistance Training. RT is weight training. If you return to the short list of why we need physical activity, increasing our RMR and adding deposits to our "bone bank" are on that list. Weight—or resistance—training gives you your best opportunity to increase glycogen storage, increase your muscle mass (a pound of muscle may utilize 50 times the amount of calories a pound of fat does; this doesn't make fat "bad," it is just doing its job). One of the best resistance movements we can do are squats or half-squats. This movement impacts the largest muscle groups in the body—gluteals, quadriceps, and hamstrings—and is a great way to utilize stored calories, develop more glycogen storage, and help to keep the muscles involved "toned." (Tone has little to do with appearance; it means that each muscle is at its proper length). You don't need a squat rack or a 45-pound bar with plates to do squats. You can use hand weights, no weights, or a wall to do measured movement where you hold the squat during the lower position. You also don't need a gym membership. Knees permitting, back permitting, hips permitting—this is a great movement to do at home.

Progressive Resistance Training (PRT) is the idea that you will increase your weight—or resistance—as you progress. You've mastered incline presses with 20-pound dumbbells doing 3 sets of 10 repetitions. Time to progress. Use 25 pounds with 4 sets and 7 repetitions each. You're able to squat 3 X 10 with five-pound dumbbells in your hand—pick up ten-pound weights and do 3 X 7 and progress until you get up to the 3 X 10. Then increase the weight and lower the repetitions again until you can comfortably return to the 3 X 10 level.

For beginning resistance/weight trainers, 90% of any cosmetic change will happen in the first 6 to 9 months of training. But this hasn't stopped legions of people from doing the same weight training routine year after year without honoring FAIS and doing a continuous "fooling" of their body by learning to swim, ride a bike, climbing stairs, etc.

Females have a long way to go, in terms of numbers, to catch up to men in training with weights. That means females have the most to gain. In a previous study, women between the ages of 55 and 65 who started RT were able to increase both spine bone density and hip bone density by 1% and .9% while a control group lost 2% and 1.5%. Another study in my files showed even after a 30% increase in the number of females working with weights (from 1987 to 1992), that men were using weights at a rate three times that of women. Fear not, ladies. If your concern about "getting big" is keeping you from starting a resistance training program using weights, this will not happen. What will happen is that your glycogen storage cells will be more efficient causing your RMR to increase and your exercise time will be more effective. Both sexes should add resistance training to their cardiovascular and stretching activities.

Limitations

With weight training, as with all exercise activities, we must respect the limitations we have caused by past injuries, surgeries or the term I like to use: having had too many birthdays.

I've shared I had spinal surgery when I was only 16 years old, and I've had both shoulders surgically repaired. But the most pain I ever felt happened during a pickup football game. I was on the left side rushing the punter. My friend was on the right side doing the same. The punter got the kick off and I slowed down. My friend didn't. In the backfield we "knocked knees" with him going full speed and me going only one-quarter speed. The pain I endured for 16 months with my back injury pales in comparison to the intensity of the pain I felt that day on the football field behind Paynter Middle School. I literally had tears in my eyes. Odd thing was, two hours later I had no pain. I played in the pickup game the next week. I suffered no long-term consequence except I have a tender spot behind my knee cap. Never MRI'd, never X-rayed. It prevents me from kneeling and limits the weight I can use when doing squats. Fortunately, it doesn't prevent me from riding a bike, swimming or walking up steps. So, with the odd assortment of injuries, I can't run on a track, lift heavy amounts of weight, and my flexibility is limited due to my back and shoulder issues. We are all going to have limitations to our physical activities. But there are sufficient PRT techniques, types of exercise equipment, and floor exercises to enable almost anybody with any physical limitation to have a challenging workout.

I've been a member of three fitness facilities. The best one was a true workout place. No showers, no air conditioning, a 10,000 BTU heater hanging in the corner. The clientele was a mixture of the young, urban professionals (old school term was Yuppies), artist-types, bike messengers and more tattooed people than in any other gym. There was a seated military press chair with a spotter's stand. I used to put 45-pound plates on the 45-pound bar and get a volunteer to spot me. I would do the shoulder press behind my head. My shoulders grew wide. It was my favorite lifting exercise. A friend, who was a former college football player, told me on more than one occasion, "Never lift weights over your head after your 40th birthday." On the way into surgery for my second torn rotator cuff repair, how I wished I had heeded his advice.

Exercise Equipment

During my stint selling exercise equipment, I was often asked, "What is the best piece of equipment to own?" My stock answer became, "The one you're going to use." I know that many of the steppers, treadmills, home gym units, ski machines, and recumbent bikes I sold became clothes hangers and dust collectors not too long after I sold them. When people buy a piece of equipment, they tend to have unrealistic hope for what that equipment will do for them or how their body will change. If you have the finances and the room to set up a home gym, I wouldn't start with a treadmill or home gym unit. I would start with a set of dumbbells—maybe from 5 pounds to 50 pounds, and I would add a bench that can go from flat to incline and a floor mat. A quality treadmill would then be the next item as you can change the intensity through the incline and the speed. And if walking is all you want to do, perfect. When I sold equipment, the treadmills I sold were priced over $2,000. And this was in 1992. I was able to sell treadmills because I took the time to learn their value. Buyers could have gone to Sears (remember them?) or to a sporting goods store and buy a treadmill for $400 to $500. But I was able to explain why a $2,000 treadmill was the way to go. It had to do with the motor (intermittent movement vs. continuous movement), and the belt (a quality belt keeps 85% of the impact in

72

the bed of the machine vs. the 100% that your joints absorb when running on the street). I would have failed any physics class I walked into but I could still discuss the "friction coefficient" well enough to sell you an expensive treadmill. For the home gym, I would also add resistance bands and loops. As a swimmer with two repaired rotator cuffs, I have to use bands each day in order to remain a swimmer.

Speaking of equipment, one thing I recently was introduced to is an activity tracker. The $44 I spent on my first one was a great investment. It tracks the number of steps I take per day, heart rate, blood pressure, oxygen level, and even records the quality of my sleep. The step counter, as I've learned, is also an application on smartphones. My second activity tracker allows me to set the timer when I'm starting a bike ride or a session in the swimming pool. I recently was able to swim 500 yards in less than nine minutes. My activity tracker was of extreme importance in lowering my time. I haven't hit that time in 25 years. I can even connect to GPS when going on a bike ride or walk and then check on the app what my course was and the elevation I climbed. I would suggest everybody own one of these activity trackers. I think the features will continue to improve. I was on a webinar recently where a physician discussed using data from the tracker to notify the wearer that their heart rate has increased ever so slightly while at rest. As was explained, this is an early indication of a medical issue.

But beware. Activity trackers may exacerbate EB. I know two women who are obsessed with counting their steps. One does 16,000 and the other one must do 20,000—*per day*. The woman walking 20,000 steps walks with a stress fracture in one of her feet. When somebody she knows is finished with a walking boot, she takes it. I've seen her walking in the neighborhood wearing the boot. If 1,750 steps equals one mile for me, she's walking ten or more miles. Imagine the things she's not doing in her life because of the time—and pain—she has to deal with in order to get all those steps in. Maybe the next generation tracker will be able to alert the wearer that their activity level is pushing them in Exercise Bulimia territory (and I'm not kidding).

Do not be unrealistic with your physical activity time. Know that you will not change your ticket in the Genetic Lottery. Understand why it is important to maintain an active lifestyle while avoiding becoming EB, and not falling victim to FAIS. Know that time devoted to physical activity should add to your life's purpose—not subtract from it.

Personal Trainers

Speaking of unrealistic expectations, I know more personal trainers than I need to know.

I had a friendly relationship with the top trainer in the city before he passed away. He had been Mr. Pittsburgh two different times. Before he got his private studio in an upscale part of the city, he trained his mostly female clients at various gyms around town. He always wore Gargoyle sunglasses to mask his jaundiced eyes and would drive his two-door Jaguar, Jeep Wrangler, or chopped Harley to his appointments. On a few occasions, he referred his clients to me to answer their questions about nutrition or supplements. His clients tended to be middle-aged females with the money—and time—to utilize his services. It was a status symbol for upscale females to have this upscale gentleman as their personal trainer. But he was the exception and not the rule.

Most of the trainers I know aren't trying to make their clients more effective and efficient with their physical activity time. Most trainers aren't trying to teach clients that the Genetic Lottery can't be overcome no matter how many $45 per hour sessions the client signs up for. Most trainers mistakenly overuse this term "burn fat". No trainer would tell a client that fat oxidizes instead of burns because they probably don't know. Most trainers are dangerous when it comes to dispensing nutrition and supplement advice. ("Don't worry about eating that *(fill in the blank)*. You'll just burn it off."). No trainer I know would explain the short—but invaluable—list of reasons why we need physical activity to their clients. No trainer would tell a client to start swimming or cycling because the trainer makes no money from that. In "There Used to Be a Bookstore," I shared the main reason a person utilizes calories is to keep their body temperature constant. Some of the most invigorating workouts I've had occurred on cold days when I bundled up and went outside for a bike ride or a long walk. No trainer gets paid when a client does that. So, instead, trainers promote Exercise Bulimia among gym-bound clients.

In the fitness facility I use, I've overheard trainers and their clients discussing such pressing matters as last night's TV watching and the upcoming Steelers game. I've seen clients, while being trained, run to check their cell phone between sets. You just don't know who texted in the previous three minutes, right? In my facility, you can easily identify the personal trainer's dream, The Human ATM. These are people who have the resources to pay a trainer an ongoing fee for months of sessions. Many trainers know me. They know I am an investment advisor, a writer, and that I also teach writing. No trainer has ever called and said, "Ken, I have money that needs to be invested. Can you teach me about the investment industry?" or "Ken, I want to share my experiences and insights with others. I want to write a book about my unique approach to training. Can I sign up for your class?"

Now that I've provided insight in the personal training hack, let me share this: if you've never trained with weights, or it's been a while since you have, it may benefit you to spend some time with a trainer to introduce or refresh yourself with the range of motion, to experiment with the level of weights you should start with, when you know it's time to increase weight and to know the difference between muscle fatigue (a good thing) and connective tissue pain (a bad thing). Likewise, if you have limitations from past injuries or a degenerative disease, there would be benefit in using the services of a skilled trainer to put together a workout plan for you. A few sessions—and not the three times per week indefinitely—will be what you need. And there wouldn't be an issue reengaging with that trainer once every three months or so.

My favorite personal trainer story is about a trainer that used to work at my facility. While most trainers won the Genetic Lottery and already have the body type that their clients want, this trainer was the exception. She had the physique of a powerlifter. She would engage with her clients on the second floor of the building. My main activity was swimming but on occasion I would go to the second floor to run a mile on the treadmill to help my breathing in the pool. I was walking to the exit when I passed this trainer talking to her coworker. I heard her say, "With my knowledge of training techniques and supplementation, I can overcome anybody's genetics." I wish I would have stopped and told her that if what she said is true, that I would give her ten times her fee if she could make me one inch taller. Unlike the trainer I introduced at the beginning of this section, she is not the exception but the rule.

<u>Yoga</u>

In this book, I have avoided—and will continue to do so—listing a specific age as the definition of "old". While there are certain behaviors people have that are stereotypical of elderly people, I will not list those. But I will share my personal opinion of when I will be old.

I will be old when two things happen: when my walking stride (or "gait") shortens and when I do not have the ability to easily get down on the floor and get back up.

My concern with my stride probably comes from my back injury. Until my surgery, I walked with a limp on my left side. At times, I would drag my foot. Before my proper diagnosis and surgery, there were times I thought I would go through life with that limp. The ability to put one foot in front of the other and walk is much appreciated by me. And there is some basis for us to do whatever we can to maintain our stride. A study of nearly 35,000 people aged 65 years or older found that individuals who walked at about 2.6 feet per second lived more years than their average life expectancy. With each increase of around 4 inches per second, the chance of dying in the next decade fell by about 12%. (*American Medical Association*; January 5, 2011).

I currently have the ability to hit the floor and pop back up again. And I want to maintain that ability for as long as possible. As with keeping my gait, there is also basis for this from the world of epidemiology. Women from Okinawa have the longest life expectancy of any ethnic group. They live a spartan lifestyle and eat their meals on the floor. One of the theories for the longevity of Okinawan women is the strength, flexibility and balance maintained by making at least three roundtrip visits to the floor each day.

That brings me to the "bad news/good news" part of this chapter. As we age, our connective tissue contracts, our spinal columns compress, and our risk of falling and getting injured increases. The good news: all of those items can be delayed or offset by incorporating a yoga practice in our lives. There is no better physical activity you can engage in than stretching your core muscles, and using your own body weight to achieve Resistance Training (a side plank in yoga requires much strength and stamina).

I knew I would eventually have to become a regular yoga student. When I started classes, my surgeries made it difficult to perform certain movements. Many of the other students were advanced. But I stuck with it and in the same way regular writing days and times turns a practice into a habit, yoga became a habit for me. Yoga has made a difference with the flexibility in my lower back and the shoulder work has made me a better swimmer. If I could only do one physical activity, I wouldn't even hesitate when choosing yoga.

The quality of a yoga class is made by the teacher. Some of the teachers I've had came only slightly prepared. They had to pause during the class to think of the next movement. Other teachers allowed students to talk during the class. This last one is presented here because in addition to working on my yoga practice, I also strive to be more consistent with my Transcendental Meditation practice. Many TM practitioners also are yoga students. The time in yoga class should be meditative, and it will only be that way if the teacher's voice is the only one heard. The good teachers separate themselves from the not-so-good teachers by their preparation and with their words early in the class.

A few years ago, I tried to introduce "Switch Week" at the facility I belong to. It would be one week where the members would do an activity that was new to them. It would introduce muscleheads to the swimming pool, spinners to the weight room, and introduce everybody to yoga. It would have been a fun way to introduce the concepts of Exercise Bulimia and Fat Aerobics Instructor Syndrome to the membership. I say "would have been" because the staff at the facility didn't get behind the idea. A great opportunity to introduce yoga to the members who would have benefited from it most was missed.

The fitness industry (gyms, trainers, supplement companies) doesn't market the benefits of physical activity I listed in this chapter. They market weight loss as the key to happiness and good health. In doing so, the industry creates millions of people who are Exercise Bulimic and waste vast amounts of time and money fighting a losing battle against the Genetic Lottery.

But, as it turns out, your weight has limited impact on your health assessment. In Part Three of this series, we will have a detailed look at the correlation between weight and health assessment, the Bouncing Body-Mass Index (BMI) and the financial incentive behind telling you that you are not healthy unless you weigh less than you do now. Stay tuned.

How To Be Old

CHAPTER SIX

Adventures in the Nutrition Trade
(...confessions of a pill pusher)

As shared earlier, it was right after I finished the editing and layout for *Cut Your Calories...Now!!* that I got the idea for this book. I thought about all the things I had written previously and realized they pointed to *How To Be Old* as my next project. CYCN details how I became interested in the study of nutrition, my experiences in the nutrition trade, why nutrition advice is constantly contradictory and 40 different ways for the reader to reduce their calorie consumption. Since the book was self-published on Amazon, three more calorie cutting methods crossed my desk. My knowledge and interest in the nutrition industry are closely tied to my knowledge and interest in the supplement industry. I'm not going to rewrite CYCN here—you have easy access to it—but I will tell you it is the most relevant book for a person living in today's world who has an interest in food, the food industry, and ways to reduce their calorie consumption while finding and maintaining satiety. What I am going to do is to explain the unique journey that lead to me acquiring the nutrition and supplement knowledge I have and how the book came to be written.

If you think the fitness industry is loaded with studies—funded by the government, by the non-profit sector and by that industry itself, there are ten times as many studies connected to the nutrition industry. I came along at the opportune time when I first applied the techniques of economic analysis and my skills as an investment researcher to the study of nutrition, after returning from my work assignment in Gainesville, Florida, in 1991.

This is what was going on at "my" time: The Nutrition Labeling and Education Act of 1990 was in place, requiring food manufacturers to begin labeling their products in May of 1993, the United States Department of Agriculture (USDA) Food Pyramid was released—after years of negotiation with various industry members over their location and size on the pyramid, and the Dietary Supplement Health and Education Act of 1994 (DSHEA) was being negotiated.

Of those three items, it was the supplement legislation that would have the most impact on me personally and professionally.

When I started doing my presentations on the "value of nutrition," I was received in a positive manner. Nobody had ever talked about the food industry the way I did. I thought I had the beginnings of a unique business—one that I had incredible passion for and would be in high demand.

But I was wrong. After my initial traction, some positive reviews and radio appearances, my progress stopped. I was trying to book presentations through HR departments of large corporations. What I heard was, "Ken, we believe in wellness. But we don't want to hear from you. We're going to call Bally's Fitness and have them send over trainers to talk to our employees about wellness." I also heard, "No thanks, Ken. We'd rather call GNC and have them send somebody to talk about which supplements our employees should be using." I reached a point where there wasn't much going on. I was in the investment business but I didn't have that many clients. I had to keep the doors open. During the time I was learning about nutrition, I was also learning about supplements, that industry, and the impact of the newly-enacted DSHEA.

A start-up company located on the outside of town was hiring people to market bodybuilding supplements to gyms throughout the US. I called and introduced myself to the owner, and told him the work I had been doing in the nutrition industry. I also shared my knowledge of the supplement industry. The fact I was training with weights was a positive.

I arranged an interview and drove to the company's office. It was in the basement of an old shoe store, about an hour east of town. The owner of the company was a former bodybuilder from California. His plan was to set up an organization to sell creatine, whey protein, pre-workout drinks, and related product to gym owners. The owners would put a markup on the products and sell them to their members. Since the DSHEA was now in effect, these products could be marketed and sold with no FTC or FDA restrictions. It was open season for those in the supplement business.

My territory was the midwestern part of the U.S. I sat at a desk in the basement of the former shoe store. A computer monitor was in front of me. The owner of the company was a marketing genius. He had obtained a computer file containing the names of all the gyms in the country. The list of the gyms in the respective territories was in my computer and those of the other sales people working the other regions. A gym name and number would appear on the screen. I would call the gym and try to speak with somebody who had the authority to buy supplements. It was a slow process at first. I could use the program to make notes on who I talked to, what we talked about and then added a note to the file with what future date to call back.

The owner of the company knew how to sell. He knew how to talk to gym owners. One of the other sales people was from New York and had also been a bodybuilder. He knew gym owners in his city and got some quick sales. I was not used to computers, didn't own one at the time, and would have issues with the program shutting down or going haywire. It was embarrassing for me to be doing this job. The one positive was that the location was far from where I lived and the chances of somebody seeing me walking into the old shoe store were small.

It is said that consistency of purpose is the key to success. After a few calls and discussing areas of common interest to build rapport with certain owners of large gyms, I started selling. Gyms in St. Louis, Columbus, Cincinnati, and various places in Chicago. I started receiving large orders from Guns Gym in the Windy City (I'm sure if that gym still exists the name was changed long ago). When I had some success, the embarrassment declined a bit but selling supplements wasn't what I should have been doing.

The phone calls started coming the other way. Gym owners were calling me. I could suggest ways for them to sell creatine, "Stackers," "Ultimate Orange" and other products to their members. We could be creative in packaging our deals. A common practice was to throw in a free container of a high-priced item. When the gym owner sold it, he recouped the shipping costs. We had access, on a limited basis, to Otomix shoes. These were the favorite of bodybuilders and weightlifters. On larger deals, we could give a deep discount on a pair of these shoes to a gym owner. I would make it seem like it was a major hassle to get these shoes and discount them, but the buyers loved those shoes so much that they helped me sell. Starting with zero clients, I grew to having 105 gym owners who bought from me. And many of them were regular buyers.

Before I tell you how I was able to get out of the supplement business, I want to share some of my favorite memories. While the owner of the company was talented at bodybuilding, supplements, and selling, he wasn't the most honorable person. He had a knee injury that caused him to limp. The owner of the building was an elderly retired shoemaker named Tony. Tony had a bad hip and walked with a limp. The owner of the company would make Tony jump through hoops to get the rent check. The owner would give Tony a certain date and time to come into the store for the check and then not be there. Tony was in the store a lot more than he should have been. We could hear the bell on the door upstairs when it opened and then hear the thud of a person with a limp walking across the floor. As we would hear the person limping down the stairs, we didn't know if it was Tony coming in search of his rent check or the owner of the company until they reached the basement.

Our desks were arranged around the outside of the basement. We could look at each other and talk about our respective theories on lifting weights, supplements, and females between phone calls. The location of this operation was in an area where many fast food restaurants had stores. There was also a Chinese restaurant that sold to-go items in large tin plates. Many times, my fellow sales people would be talking to a gym owner in another state extolling the virtues of using creatine or Ultimate Orange. They would explain that their body fat percentage went below 10% and they increased their bench press by 20 pounds because of supplements—all the while holding onto a Big Mac or with a tin plate full of Chicken Chow Mein in front of them, half eaten. That's how deals were closed.

When we were hired at this company, we were paid an hourly wage plus a commission. After a certain time period, the hourly wage was supposed to be increased. On the Friday afternoon before the increase was to take effect, the owner called a meeting. He told us that his expenses were greater than he thought they would be and the phone company charges were eating into his profits. The wage increase was going to be delayed. However, since we were selling, our commissions would help us until the wage increase occurred.

That day, upon leaving the basement, I watched as the owner limped to his old Acura and limped away. Monday morning, when we showed up to push pills and powders, the owner arrived in a new Mercedes. One of my fellow sales people asked the owner why we didn't get our pay raise and he got a new Mercedes. "You don't understand. I bought this with my personal money," was his reply. "The business money is separate from my personal money." So I certainly understand accounting and business formation and his statement was true but the appearance with the new car was demeaning to the sales staff.

We didn't have or take possession of the supplements we sold. There was a distributor located across the river from us. The orders would be sent to the distributor's warehouse and fulfilled from there. The manufacturers sold to the distributor. The companies in the industry then were Twinlabs, SportPharma, Champion Nutrition, EAS (started by a former steroid seller), MET-Rx, Weider and others long forgotten.

Creatine was popular at the time. If you are not aware, creatine is found in the mitochondria of each cell and is the "energy" part of the cell. Taking supplemental creatine provides more energy during a workout by producing more ATP (adenosine triphosphate) and enables the user to lift heavier weight for a longer period. Creatine does do this. It works as advertised. But it is also a "cell voluminizer," meaning it deposits water in parts of the body. Problem is, you don't get to tell the water where to go. I know many people who started using creatine and were surprised to find the sides of their abdomens ("obliques") were getting bigger instead of their biceps or chest.

Before I entered the business, a study was underway to determine which company was selling the purest creatine. I made phone friends with an employee of a gym owner in St. Louis. He was the one who told me about the study. At the end of one of his orders he told me the study was going to be completed the following week. I asked if it was okay if I called him for the results. This was a major study— about to have major impact on the supplement industry. The gentleman agreed to share the results.

When I called the next week and got the man on the phone, all he did was whisper to me, "SportPharma." But he had a bit of a speech impediment and it sounded like "Spaht-Faa-ma". He whispered this top-secret information because we didn't know who could be listening in to get the results of such an important study. What he and I didn't know at the time was there was only one laboratory in America making creatine. Supplement companies would come up with a catchy name, an intriguing bottle design and label, and then tell the lab what percentage of creatine that wanted in the product. Everything else was filler.

When the manufacturers of these various products saw we were having some success selling to gym owners, they did what any company in a less than honorable business would do—they started selling directly to our buyers. Our suppliers became our competitors. There were so many markups (or margins) in that industry that drug dealers were envious. The manufacturers saw an opportunity to cut out a player and keep another margin for themselves.

Near the end of my brief—but illustrious—time in the bodybuilding supplement industry, the owner of the distribution company that shipped our products sent his wife and young daughter to the basement of the old shoe store. The young girl was selling Christmas gift wrapping for a school project. I put an order in for no other reason than to keep peace in the basement. As the wife and young girl started up the steps, it dawned on me that the wrapping paper and gift bags I bought probably had more value than any of the products I was selling to gym owners.

Before I received that wrapping paper, I was out of the business. At some point, I had written an article about the importance of investors paying low fees on their assets. It's a subject that, while having gotten more attention in recent years, was buried back then. I had submitted the article to the *Pittsburgh Business Times*. Without them giving me any advance notice, they published the article. Of course, being the PBT they had to change my title, do some editing that wasn't needed, and misspell my last name. But my voice was heard.

I found out that the article was published when the owner of the supplement company put the newspaper on my desk. I was on the phone when he did so. He knew I was an investment advisor. He wasn't angry. I think he knew he caught me at a bad time in my life—and I think he knew my talents were far above the basement of that old shoe store.

I ended up getting investment clients because of that article, including a gentleman who had recently retired as an executive at one of the main health insurance companies in the city. Now, I had contacted his former company trying to market my preventive health presentations on numerous occasions. My calls were never returned.

When he learned that I had an interest in nutrition and fitness, he arranged for me to meet the woman at his former company who oversaw so-called wellness programs (it will be forever difficult for me to write the word "wellness"). I went to this meeting with anticipation. I got a great new client AND I was getting a chance to present my unique approach to nutrition to a person who was getting paid to be interested in the subject.

But the woman was not interested in me or my story. I quickly learned she only took the meeting because her former superior asked her to. She did not spend one moment trying to determine if there was value in my approach to nutrition and fitness. She did, however, teach me one thing. She taught me what a "Duchenne smile" was. This is the type of smile when a person smiles with their mouth but not their eyes. An insincere smile. The woman I met was unprofessional, disrespectful, insincere and had mean eyes.

If this section of this chapter was a movie, this part would be the montage. I ask you to think of the training scene in the first *Rocky* movie. I want to remind you of what happened to me from the time I left Ms. Duchenne's office until I was given the opportunity to write *Cut Your Calories...Now!!*

So, with the theme from *Rocky* playing in your head, here's the montage that covered 14 or so years of my life:

- Began travel to Cuba (seven of my 10 trips during this time)
- Six trips to Asia
- Five trips to Europe
- A seven-year journey to see 36 of the 37 paintings attributed to Dutch Master Johannes Vermeer
- Trips to WWII sites Normandy, Bastogne, the River Kwai and Iwo Jima
- The beginning, middle, and end of a beautiful eight-year romance with a beautiful, intelligent and sexy female. To date, the great romance of my life
- Most of the 15 articles published in the *Pittsburgh Post-Gazette* written during this time
- Expansion of my investment practice and development of a CPA-accredited class in Investor Psychology

OK, montage over. Back to the story.

In the middle of 2013, I found myself with only three Vermeer paintings to see. One was in Ireland, one was in Scotland and one was in the storage area of Buckingham Palace. The first two were in public galleries so there was no issue in seeing them; the third was off limits to me. My first email to the young lady who oversaw the Royal Art Collection was met with an immediate, "Thank you for your interest but there is no way you could see this painting." It took two heartfelt, sincere and well-thought out emails before I was told I could see this painting—but only if I passed the background check (which I did!). In Chapter Two, I shared some of the ancillary benefits of writing. The only reason I was able to get a private tour of an invaluable painting in the basement of Buckingham Palace was my ability to write.

When I returned from this legendary trip (I was also able to see Sigmund Freud's studio in London and spend two amazing days in Glasgow, Scotland) in September of 2013, I thought about what project I wanted to tackle next. And the way I left the nutrition trade—with a Duchenne smiling woman wanting me out of her office—was always a sore point with me. I still had passion for the subjects of nutrition and fitness. Over the years I put ideas and notes about nutrition and fitness education, stories on weight loss scams, and ideas for reducing calories in a blue Walmart plastic crate. On back-to-back freezing cold weekends in February of 2014 I went through that crate. When I had been doing nutrition presentations, I supplied a handout that listed 12 ways for the reader to reduce their calories. As I sorted through the material I had accumulated, that list had grown to 36 different calorie cutting ideas.

I organized my "library" and wrote the outline for an updated presentation. On my previous stint, it was not difficult to go to places and do presentations based on the way I was learning about nutrition. The cassette copies I made of one of my radio interviews helped (that interview also helped the interviewer get a better job at a bigger station). When people heard me talk about nutrition like it had never been discussed, it was easy for a person to invite me to speak to their group. As I write this, I'm still dismayed that my progress had stopped in 1996; but it is my history and I could not—or would not—change the things that happened to me since that time. But this time, it was near impossible. When I tried to arrange free presentations on nutrition and my unique story, certain individuals who are compensated to teach others to lead a healthy lifestyle, banded together and blocked my efforts. Tough news for me? No way. It was those select people getting compensated to teach others about a healthy lifestyle (and doing a poor job of it) that gave me the epiphany I needed in order to write *Cut Your Calories...Now!!* If that crew had been doing a proper job, there would have been no need for me. I wouldn't have had anything unique or new to write about the subject of nutrition.

CYCN opens with an insightful and entertaining prologue and ends with an equally insightful and entertaining epilogue. Sandwiched in between are 40 (up from the revised 36) ways for you to reduce your calorie consumption while finding satiety (the feeling of "full"). Those 40 ways are broken down into the Economics of Calorie Cutting, the Physical Aspects of Calorie Cutting, the Mental Aspects of Calorie Cutting, and the Social and Media Aspects of Calorie Cutting. Want to know what to eat and how? At any age? It's in *Cut Your Calories...Now!!*

A question often asked: "Should I take supplements?" And that answer will be "no". Since the passage of the DSHEA in 1994, the industry has grown from $8 billion in annual sales to over $40 billion. It is now possible for you and me to put sugar pills in a bottle, come up with cool label art work, a catchy product name and market the worthless pills to the public. As long as we don't make medicinal claims for our sugar pills, there is no government oversight into what we are doing. And the value we would be offering is nonexistent.

The other side of the fence—those that have a financial interest in you taking supplements—would trot out the tired list of reasons why you need supplements. That list of claims is below, followed by my answers.

"Food is not food any more. The soil has been depleted."
While the composition of the soil has been changing due to climate, fertilizer, crop rotation and other farming methods, a carrot today matches up with a carrot from 50 years ago. If the soil was dramatically different, today's carrot wouldn't be a carrot; it would be a different food product. A change in the

fiber, mineral, vitamin and water content would mean a different end result. And somebody would have to come up with a different name (The supplement industry is good at coming up with names—it's style over substance in that business.)

"They're using too many pesticides. We need supplements to protect ourselves!"
A crowd favorite. While pesticides are part of today's large scale farming operation (and a key reason why produce is as affordable as it is), the main source of pesticides comes from the growing product itself. Growing produce provides its own natural substances to protect itself from pests, bugs, etc. And, on a related note, organic food can use pesticides from an approved list of pesticides and maintain its "organic" labeling.

"There's too many chemicals in the food!"
News flash—there's chemicals in everything. Life is chemistry. Ever eaten a banana? Then you've consumed the naturally occurring formaldehyde occurring in the fruit. Like apples? Still going to like them when I tell you they contain a chemical called acetaldehyde? With all chemicals, especially naturally occurring ones, there is no need to "supplement" them away. These chemicals are part of the process and the end product. The dose makes any chemical harmless or harmful.

"We're eating too much sugar/fat/dairy. We need supplements!"
While it is true that the typical person overconsumes all of the above, it is faulty thinking to suppose a multi-vitamin, multi-mineral pill in a bottle that costs pennies to make and is sold for dollars will offset the excess sugar/fat/dairy consumption. On a related note: 1/3 of vegetables consumed by Americans are French-fried potatoes.

"My Aunt Gladys wasn't feeling well. Then she started taking supplements. Now she's powerlifting and running the high hurdles!"
I've heard this one for years in various forms with various family members. And while I can't discount the placebo effect, I think the idea that Aunt Gladys, who may be suffering from some undiagnosed illness, can "supplement" that illness away is

silly. A nutritional deficiency may be the result of an illness and not the cause. The bioavailability of whatever supplements Gladys is taking is questionable and, when it comes to supplements, "more is not more". Inundating your system with multiple times the Recommended Daily Allowance is not like putting more money into an investment plan. The body can only assimilate a finite amount of any nutrient. The remainder is eliminated (one of the reasons why Americans have some of the most nutrient-dense urine in the world). Aunt Gladys, and others like her, would be better off by reading CYCN and enrolling in yoga classes.

When I think or write about the "placebo" effect, I always think of a story from the other side of the fence—the "nocebo" effect. A young man was enrolled in a double-blind study. He was given a bottle of pills and was told to take one pill four times per day. He didn't know if he had the pharmaceutical agent under study or the sugar pills. He gets into an argument with his girlfriend. She threatens to leave him. He threatens suicide. As the girl is leaving, the guy swallows the entire bottle of pills from the study. He starts stumbling around the house, telling the girl he feels like passing out. He does just that. She calls the ambulance. Paramedics work to bring the fellow's blood pressure up. He doesn't stabilize. He's out. Blood pressure falls. Paramedics bring it back up. The girl shows the paramedics the empty bottle of pills and tells the medics about the study. The paramedics, in between sessions of stabilizing the guy, contact a doctor connected to the study. The doctor reports that the guy is not taking the active medicine; he is in the control group. As the guy is fading in and out of consciousness, the medics tell him that he swallowed a bunch of sugar pills. His BP stabilizes, he regains total consciousness and the paramedics leave him and his (I'm sure ex-) girlfriend to work things out.

The classic supplement story happened during my first tour of duty in the nutrition trade.

I did back-to-back nutrition presentations at a large law firm in downtown Pittsburgh. I was in the firm's auditorium. Half of the workers came to the first session and the other half came to the second. As the firm had employees with hearing issues, a woman stood next to me translating my words into sign language. I had receptive audiences from the start both times.

At the end of the first session, a woman asked a question, "Should I take supplements?"

My answer was similar to this, "If you eat too much sugar, too much trans fatty acids, and too much in general, and if you don't eat enough fiber, essential fatty acids, if you smoke cigarettes, if you don't get quality sleep, if you don't have enough physical activity in your life, and if you live with too much stress, then there is not one pill, powder, potion, mixer, or elixir that is going to do you one bit of good." Now, I'll stand by that statement forever and the only people that will launch an argument are sellers of supplements.

After the presentation, a woman approached me and told me she had the proper idea on how to use supplements. As I was—and am—always trying to learn, I asked her what her idea was. She replied, "I only take supplements on the days that I eat at fast food restaurants." Now, I have told that story to groups and individuals over the years. Many times, when somebody has heard the idea of "canceling" a Big Mac or Whopper with a pill, they get a look on their face that says, "Wow! What a great idea!" But it's not. It's a silly idea. *(A related story comes from the Finnish Smokers study. Male cigarette smokers between the ages of 50 and 69 who were given beta carotene (precursor to Vitamin A) supplements had more incidence of lung cancer than those smokers with zero supplementation).*

Before I close off the section on supplements, I want to share one thing: at any given time, I could reenter the industry and be successful. I know how to think up names of products, I know who to market them to, I know how to play on the fears and body-image issues of the population and I know how and where to get my supplements bottled and packaged. But I have no interest in putting my toe into those murky waters ever gain. Please think about that the next time you see an advertisement for the next supplement that will help you lose weight, gain muscle, prevent heart disease, cancer, diabetes, etc.

Final Thoughts on the Supplement Industry

Six Months from Now

The industry must reinvent itself on a regular basis. There are players in the industry who know the top selling supplement six months from now. You haven't heard of the product yet but the bottles and labels are done, the marketing campaign is being worked on and social media will help introduce this new product to the world. The reason why a new product must be introduced every six months is the one introduced six months ago didn't actually do what it was touted to do.

Orrin Hatch

Orrin Hatch, when he was a sitting U.S. Senator from Utah, was the politician most credited with getting the DSHEA of 1994 legislation passed. When he announced his retirement from the Senate, I wrote an article for the *Pittsburgh Post-Gazette*. That article, "Orrin Hatch's Legacy is a Tough Pill to Swallow," was written so I could share my two connections with Orrin. It turns out that Hatch and I—in addition to having supplement industry experience— graduated from the same high school. Hatch graduated many years before I did and, unlike me, made it into the Baldwin High School Sports Hall of Fame. As was shared by Marion Nestle, PhD (*Food Politics*), the nation's leading nutrition educator after reading the article, "Hatch has a lot to answer for." And he really does. *(Article is available online and on my website.)*

"A Special Place in Hell"

I appreciate the emotional toll illness can take on an individual and a family. Not all treatments work for all diagnosed ailments because medicine is not an exact science. I equally appreciate someone diagnosed with a condition trying to learn as much as they can about that condition. But most people don't get on the best possible learning curve. They detour to alternative treatments. And, as Paul Offit, M.D., wrote in his insightful book about the scam of the supplement industry (*Do You Believe in Magic?*) there is no alternative medicine. There is treatment that works and treatment that doesn't work. If any supplement actually did its purported purpose, the manufacturer would finance a double-blind study and publish the results. If that happened, sales would explode. But that won't happen. Because there is no supplement that has benefit for the end user. It bothers me to no end when the almost totally unregulated supplement industry markets pills to improve memory, help cognitive function and prevent dementia. The American Council on Science and Health (ACSH) whose motto is "Science, not hype" published an essay about companies marketing products such as Prevagen to separate people with concerns about their cognitive ability from their money. Prevagen's slick commercials—which mimic those of FDA-approved pharmaceuticals—aside, the contents aren't going to help anybody in any stage of memory loss or dementia and may prevent them from seeking treatments that may offer some value. In the essay titled "A Special Place in Hell: Hucksters Peddle Useless Alzheimer's Supplements" the ACSH wrote this:

"If you're not convinced, perhaps this will do the trick. Alzheimer's dementia is arguably the most devastating disease of all, especially for family members who will see a loved one slowly and inexorably decline into a person who has lost virtually all mental capacity. Not only is there no cure, but, after many years of study and numerous hypotheses, we don't have the wildest idea of what causes it. Although there are drugs that supposedly delay the decline, they are marginally helpful (at best) and have a boatload of side effects. In short, nothing works."

The title is spot on. The ACSH has some of the best titles. A similar title was used for a piece about a seller of supplements who was marketing pills to parents of autistic children. In CYCN, No. 31 suggests the reader maintain a steady reading list of objective sources on nutrition, fitness and related subjects. One of my favorites is the ACSH Daily Dispatch. You can subscribe for free.

This book will have a short summary of memory issues and aging in the epilogue. In Part Three of this series, we will have a detailed look at memory, Alzheimer's disease, dementia and FTD (frontal temporal dementia). That section will define each, the differentiation between them, current diagnostic tools, and what we can do—if anything—to prevent, delay or offset diseases of the brain. Whatever can be done to improve memory and delay declines in cognitive ability, it will not be supplied by the supplement industry.

Addendum to Supplements

I can hear the supplement industry and the Multi-Level Marketers yelling now, "But what about Vitamin D?? Most people are deficient in Vitamin D! Many health problems are caused by Vitamin D deficiency!! We should all be taking supplements!!" I've had experience with Vitamin D and medically-prescribed Vitamin D. Here is something most MLMers don't share with their buyers: Vitamin D is not a vitamin; it is a pre-hormone. Your body produces cholecalciferol from sunlight interacting with a form of cholesterol in skin. That hormone is converted to calcitriol, the active form of the hormone in the body, also known as D3. D3 is then sent to the liver where an enzyme converts it to 25 (OH)D. This conversion is then sent to the kidneys where its main function is to control blood calcium and assist in governing the immune system.

People who are deficient in Vitamin/Hormone D may have other lifestyle factors (sedentary lifestyle, excess calories and alcohol, cigarettes), that show as issues attributed to Vitamin D deficiency. The simple idea that taking a manufactured pill with unknown bioavailability to replicate the unique process that involves your skin and two major organs is difficult to swallow (pun definitely intended).

As of this writing, neither the Institute of Medicine (IOH) or the United Stated Preventive Services Task Force (USPSTF) recommend Vitamin D supplementation.

As for me, I once had symptoms that put me in the office of an endocrinologist. A blood test showed a Vitamin D deficiency. I went through the medically-prescribed dosage of Vitamin D for six weeks. When the test was repeated, the doctor told me that I was no longer deficient in Vitamin D and "everything is back to normal." However, the symptoms I had remained. It was only after I addressed possible causes of the symptoms that I was able to clear them on my own. (I will share that the "cures" I used are found in this book.)

How To Be Old

CHAPTER SEVEN

The Importance of Sleep
"Sleep is the best meditation."
--The Dalai Lama

If living your life the way a writer lives is the most important thing you can do for your mental health and well-being, and being physically active without being Exercise Bulimic (and doing yoga!) is the most important thing you can do for your body, the ribbon that ties them together is sufficient, restful sleep. You must do what is necessary to become a better sleeper.

When I was younger, I could keep late night hours, grab a few hours of sleep and be back at it early the next morning. One of the reasons my travel resume is full of so many great stories is that I was up early in any city I was in to explore the people, the life, the buildings and the history, no matter how late I ended the previous night. But I know now—provided to me by experience and just the right number of birthdays—is that we need at least seven hours of quality sleep each night.

For the people who think they can function on four to five hours of sleep, I put them in the same category as the people who say they work 12 hours per day. Both are lying. Both parties may have done the minimal sleep and the long work day on few occasions but not as a regular way of life.

The idea that it is commendable to sleep only a few hours is not only unhealthy, it is unsafe. Being "underslept" (cool British term) has caused numerous car crashes, workplace accidents, and poor decision making which results in more of the first two. Not getting enough sleep (defined by six hours of sleep per night or less) results in a 55% increase in your chance of becoming obese, a 21% increase in your chance of developing elevated blood pressure and a 33% chance of developing Type II diabetes.

Sleep is necessary for your body's immune system to do the myriad of things it needs to do. Your "set point" (your healthy weight) needs sufficient sleep to work properly. Lack of sleep can also increase inflammation and deregulate your hormonal system. Lack of restful sleep can lead to weight gain. From personal experience: many times I was underslept and I spent much of the next day "chasing carbs," eating easy to digest refined carbohydrates to get the quick energy to keep doing the things I needed to do.

Think about the times you've had a cold or the flu. It was Nyquil-induced sleep that got you over the illness. Your immune system works best during sleep and any disease (acute or chronic) is better managed with proper sleep.

Your brain health is also dependent on sleep. The deregulation of hormones may contribute to increased stress and decreased pain tolerance.

If you take the advice shared earlier and start putting together writing projects, you will value the importance of sleep in two ways: your "creative soul" and subconscious works best with sufficient sleep. And writing is fatiguing. You will need regular, consistent sleep to get your best words on paper.

When I was an employee, I walked into offices many times without sufficient sleep (and a bit hungover). I wasn't a good employee on those days. As an employer, I would let an employee do that—once. And that's it. One and done. The underslept employee pushes the tough tasks aside and pursues the easy ones. The underslept employee wastes the morning in anticipation of the lunchtime bell and then wastes the afternoon waiting for the quitting bell.

(I was that employee but would never tolerate it as an employer.)

So, you get the point. You need quality sleep and you may need to work on your "sleep game". The American Academy of Sleep Medicine and Sleep Research Society, the National Sleep Foundation, the American Thoracic Society, and the American Heart Association all recommend a minimum of seven hours of sleep. Few people need less; many need another hour or so.

The foundation for a proper night's sleep can be found in Chapter Four, "How Do You Spend Your Days?" If your days don't provide you a sense of creation and accomplishment but instead are full of stress, confrontation, ill will, poor dietary choices and excessive alcohol, you will have a difficult time obtaining proper sleep. If you don't have some sense of what you will be doing tomorrow—and all the tomorrows that follow it—you will also have a difficult time finding quality sleep. In the times in my life when I was woefully underemployed—or selling supplements—I can assure you I did not sleep well. As an investment advisor, I realized after the 2008 market decline my main job was to make sure my clients and I sleep well at night.

That's the Big Picture. Let's bring it down to things you can do immediately to make yourself you a better sleeper, and things you can stop doing that will also make you a better sleeper.

Sleep experts—and people like me keenly interested in the subject—will tell you that your bed should only be used for two things—and one of them is sleep. Your bed should not be a desk, it should not be a dining area, it should not be a place to watch TV from, and it should not be a resting spot for clothes, books, and whatever else you pile on during the day. Get your TV out of your room. An hour or so before I go to sleep, I turn on a small light in my bedroom and turn down the cover. In the remaining hour of my day I know my bed is waiting for me.

On a personal note, I've noticed that if I'm out at night (at a meeting or for a walk) and return home an hour or so before going to sleep, I sleep better. There is no scientific reason why that is (note: I'm talking about a night out with no alcohol—see below).

You should not have your cell phone in your bedroom. People will say they use their phone for their alarm. Get another method to wake up. Even with your ringer "off" you subconsciously know your phone is within reach. Your subconscious tells you, "Hey, if you wake up in the middle of the night, you can check messages or cruise the internet!" And that's what will happen. My old cell has no service but the alarm still works. My current phone is not near me when I sleep. Same rules apply for laptops and tablets.

What is near me is my clock radio, tuned to a station with overnight talk. Nothing too detailed or serious. If I wake up in the middle of the night, I wake up at three levels. Level 1 is I realize I'm awake but I know I will fall right back to sleep. Level 2 is I'm awake and more awake than Level 1. I hit the "Sleep" (how appropriate) button on the clock radio. Lightweight banter on the radio puts me back to sleep and the radio shuts off in 30 minutes. Level 3 is when I wake and I'm not going right back to sleep. For these times, I tend to have a book I'm reading in progress. The book is not too detailed or one that requires intense concentration. It is light reading of a subject I'm interested in: movies, economics, healthcare. Depending on my level of "awake" I get out of bed, move to another room where the book is and read for 20-30 minutes before returning to "sleep" stage and going back to bed. By the way, one of life's simple pleasures happens in Level 1. It's those times when you wake up at 4:15 a.m. on your way to falling right back to sleep knowing your alarm won't be going off until 6:00 a.m.

There is a concept of "segment" sleep where a person is up for extended periods throughout the night. There is nothing abnormal about people who sleep in this way. I have, at periods in my adult life, been a segment sleeper. It was during one of those times that I started to keep easy reading material next to my reading chair. A segment sleeper may still get sufficient sleep but it comes in "shifts" (for lack of a better term).

I'm a meditation student. My practice asks me to devote 20 minutes per day, twice per day in meditation. Many times in my practice, I've fallen asleep during this period. The instructors will report that is not an issue; my body was fatigued and I needed the rest.

My meditation naps reminded me of a story told to me years ago. Thomas Edison used to sit in his desk chair with ball bearings in his hand. His naps were the length of the time it took him to fall asleep, relax his hand, have the ball bearings hit the ground and wake him up. That short time was all Edison needed to refresh and go back to inventing (and special thanks for motion pictures, Tom).

A good nap strategy is to take one in the late afternoon of a night where you will be out and up later than normal. The length of this nap is important. Ten minutes may be too short to be refreshed. Thirty minutes may put you into REM (Rapid Eye Movement) sleep and leave you too groggy upon wakening. Twenty minutes is the ideal time for this type of nap.

Think of sleep in the same way Chapter Three asked you to install proper writing habits.

You must develop proper sleep habits in terms of preparing for sleep, what to do if you wake in the middle of the night, and a judicious use of naps. The best thing you can do in this area is have a tight window of 30 minutes or less when you go to sleep (say, 10:00 p.m. to 10:30 p.m.) as opposed to a two-hour window. In one study with data obtained from a wearable device manufacturer, individuals with the tighter window slept 35 minutes more per night than those with the less consistent bedtime.

Sleep Devices

There is money in sleep. There are products marketed to make us better sleepers. There is tremendous venture capital chasing better sleep products. Some have value and some don't.

Wearable Devices

Both of my wearables can monitor my sleep length and quality. Sleep is broken into light, restful, Rapid Eye Movement (REM) and awake. As a competitive person, I feel charged when I get over an hour of REM sleep. REM is the deepest level of sleep and the place where the most vivid dreams occur. REM is usually reached at the end of a sleep session; that's the reason why your dreams seem to happen right before you wake up. Your wearable won't make you a better sleeper like the other items in this section will. But I enjoy monitoring my sleep quality from the previous night, just as I like to check the number of steps taken or the distance and speed of a swim session.

White Noise Machines

I know people who use these machines and attest to them. I can't make any comments on them except that I would hope the users would be doing the other "pre-sleep" things on this list before going to sleep instead of relying on the white noise.

Supplements

I'm not a fan of supplements. In terms of sleep supplements, here is the reasoning: your pineal gland produces a hormone known as melatonin. It is the sleep hormone. More of it circulates at night than in the daytime, based on our circadian rhythm. The supplement industry sees melatonin supplements as an easy way to get more of your money. But taking melatonin as a supplement could cause your pineal gland to reduce or shut down the amount produced naturally (your body measures circulating hormones and can adjust up and down in the production of any of them). Any supplement may also interfere with the absorption of medically prescribed (and needed) drugs.

Snoring Devices

Anybody who was on the practice field at Baldwin High School on that hot August day many years ago saw my nose being broken in a football practice. For years, the deviated septum caused by the break made me a snorer. I've been woken by many sleep mates whose own sleep was disrupted by me. A simple move to my side cured the issue in most situations. There was a time I went to sleep with a special mask that was to prevent my mouth from opening too wide during sleep. The theory behind the mask was solid. If my mouth opened to the point that my soft palate and neck muscles relaxed too much, snoring would ensue. I never got used to wearing the mask. My snoring was greatly reduced when I had my deviated septum surgically repaired. I still have the cartilage damage in my nose but that is a more aesthetic item than a medical one. I've gone this far with it and I'll go the rest of the way with it.

I have seen a new product being marketed for snoring. It makes great use of technology and a simple theory to stop snoring. The user places a small device under their pillow. A monitor is placed near the bed. If the user's head position goes to the spot where they start snoring, the monitor messages the device under the pillow to raise the pillow level to the point where the user stops snoring. By the limited research I've done on this product, it appears to have the science and technology behind it. I'm going to stay tuned to this one.

The Thief of Sleep

Few things interfere with your sleep as much as alcohol, which is opposite of how alcohol is portrayed in media. The movie or TV shows with an inebriated person who falls asleep and can't be woken is stereotypical—and totally inaccurate. You may grow tired faster from consuming alcohol, and it will put you to sleep, but it will prevent quality REM sleep. There comes a point in life where a tradeoff has to be made: Do I want to consume alcohol or do I want quality sleep? The more birthdays you have the more votes go to the latter.

The next chapter isn't going to tell you to quit drinking. It will share some ideas on reducing your alcohol consumption as you go through the remainder of your life. But it is a rule that can't be ignored: alcohol and quality sound sleep aren't found in the same cocktail mix (pun definitely intended).

Here is my insight into alcohol and sleep: have alcohol with your dinner. Quit drinking a few hours before you go to sleep. Consume water (or Propel or Sugar-Free Gatorade) before going to sleep. Stay awake for a few hours after your last drink. As our baseball managers used to tell us when we got hit by a pitch or a bad hop, "Walk it off." Go to sleep when your buzz is behind you; take a walk after drinking and before turning in. Try to consume your alcohol on a night before a day when you have the luxury of sleeping a bit later. More on this subject in the next chapter.

<u>Sleep Apnea</u>

In my snoring days, I went to a sleep clinic to see if I suffered from apnea. The setting was in a hospital room that looked more like a mid-scale hotel room. I went swimming in the evening to make sure I would be tired. After checking in and getting wired up, I went to sleep. I slept through the night and the clinician woke me at the end of the session. She told me I did snore (which I knew) but that I didn't have sleep apnea (which I was glad to hear). If you have sleep apnea, restless leg syndrome or sleep walk, these are serious—but treatable—issues. With the impact sleep has on all other aspects of life, don't ignore these issues. If you are diagnosed with sleep apnea and obtain a CPAP (Continuous Positive Airway Pressure) machine, use it. Be a compliant patient but stay on top of your situation. You may lose weight in the future which could adjust your need for such a machine. You may develop other lifestyle factors that reduce your need or frequency for the machine.

As an investment advisor, I know many stories of sellers of investment products who have taken advantage of clients. Churning of accounts, excessive fees, unsuitable, high commission products, etc. I also have access to investment newsletters that share similar stories. When I read stories about brokers who have gone undetected for a long period of time knowing they've committed crimes or taken advantage of people who entrusted them with their money, a question always comes to mind: "How did they sleep?" How did Bernie Madoff kiss the lovely Ruth Madoff good-night and fall asleep...each night for decades?

On the same hand, I know people who "robbed" banks. Not with a gun and a mask but with a piece of fiction called a real estate appraisal. When I was involved in the real estate development and banking industries there was an untitled game being played. The game involved real estate investors identifying which lenders would make loans on properties based on overinflated appraisals—and then sharing that information with other borrowers. I wondered then and I wonder now: how did those real estate investors and their appraisers sleep knowing that they were skirting the law?

There has to be a switch within a person's conscious that goes into the "off" position and enables them to sleep while doing these deeds during the day. There has to be a shutting down of a moral compass that allows some people to lie right to the face of a client or a loan officer.

Most of us, fortunately, don't have that switch or the ability to shut down right while we do wrong. So, in the same way you need to lead a positive, productive, healthy, charitable, physically active life to increase your chances of good sleep, you must also not do negative transgressions during the day—financial or otherwise—that will settle into your subconscious brain and make it more difficult to get restful sleep.

CHAPTER EIGHT

Alcohol—less is more

This is the third chapter in the third book that I've used the same subtitle to discuss alcohol. In *The Confusing Muse*, alcohol was discussed as it pertains to the world of meeting people and in dating and romance. In *Cut Your Calories…Now!!* the subject is discussed because alcohol carries a fair number of calories and, after consuming it, people tend to lose their impulse control which causes overeating. In this chapter of this book, we'll examine issues with alcohol as we get older and ways to lessen the amount of alcohol we're drinking.

Everybody has a back story and a history with alcohol. Mine is most likely different than yours. So that you can understand how I arrived at using the same title for a chapter on the subject in three books, let me share my history.

When I was coming up, alcohol was everywhere. My father and uncles loved to get together, drink beer and "shooters" (whiskey shots) and discuss issues of the day—even if they really didn't know what they were talking about! My mother's family was Serbian and there was more than enough alcohol at Serbian events—including the dangerous "slivovitz" (plum brandy). Dean Martin, Foster Brooks and others portrayed alcoholics on TV for laughs. In our family basement, there was a sign behind the bar that read, "I'm working under a handicap…I'm sober!" The older brother of one of my friends would regale us with stories of driving around South Park with a case of beer in his Dodge Challenger (the original Challenger). No wonder I couldn't wait to be old enough to drop a shot of whiskey into a beer mug and have my first boilermaker.

But when I got hurt playing football in tenth grade, my life took a major detour. I began an odyssey of 16 months of living with intense, throbbing pain in my leg. I started to drink not just because it was the thing to do and because my friends were doing it; I started to drink because it was one of the few things that quieted the pain for a few hours.

After high school and during college, I didn't let up. College was a sheer struggle for me and what may have saved me was the summer job I got driving a beer truck when my GPA at Duquesne University was 1.6. After a hard day of delivering beer, the Rolling Rocks I hid in the back of the cooler sure went down smooth. It was the difficult nature of that job and the personalities of the people I worked with that gave me the motivation to return to school under academic probation and do what I needed to do in order to graduate.

In the working world, I continued to drink my share. I came up at a time when DUI laws weren't nearly as strict as they are now. The era of large night clubs and bars was in full force. I went to those places because it was where the females were. I drove under the influence hundreds and hundreds of times. The fact I didn't get a DUI is still a minor miracle to me. My first job working in the real estate development and banking industries gave me my first taste of travel. Few things are as fun as being an unattached, reasonably attractive young man traveling on a company expense account.

It wasn't until I had the opportunity to examine my relationship with alcohol and to produce the articles and books that I produced that enabled me to obtain objectivity with regard to my romance with alcohol.

In Chapter Two I shared that I've wasted a lot of time in my life. A lot of time wasted in gyms and a lot of time wasted in clubs and bars. And excessive drinking was to be found in those clubs. The concept of having "a drink" or "less is more" was not known to me in the days of Chauncy's, the Bettis Lounge, Froggy's (but only on Friday), Donzi's, the Grove and numerous other clubs long gone or long forgotten. I finished a drink and immediately ordered another—and then another. Like a lot of young men without total self-confidence and wavering levels of self-esteem, I needed alcohol in order to "approach and open" females. My inebriation made me make some decisions I regretted and probably caused me to miss positive signals from some willing and interested females. There were times during my "ballroom days" (a favorite phrase) that I woke up after a night of debauchery either in a young woman's apartment that I needed to get out of post haste or with a puzzling level of depression. It was a combination of the alcohol and my rudderless youth that put me in those apartments; it was the alcohol that gave me post-drinking depression. I used to stay to closing time because I thought something of interest would happen and I didn't want to miss it. And even after getting shown the door, if there was an after-hours club I could get into, I stumbled into and out of it.

Alcohol is a time waster. It is also a calorie generator. Not just from the 150 calories in each bottle of beer or each glass of wine times the number of bottles or glasses consumed, but also the extra calories consumed caused by the loss of impulse control. There is another way alcohol causes an increase in calories. The previous chapter talked about "chasing carbs" if you are underslept. As that chapter detailed, alcohol consumption robs one of sleep—it doesn't add to it—and it adds to carb chasing the next day.

A few years ago, I went to see a doctor who was a general practitioner. I was going to have my rotator cuff repaired and was required to get a pre-surgery physical. The doctor saw results of a blood test and informed me that my liver enzymes were elevated and I needed to quit drinking alcohol immediately. He told me I had to become a "teetotaler". It was a word I had heard before in old movies and novels but never thought I would a hear it from a doctor (of course, he was an older person).

I made the decision that I was going to continue to drink alcohol. But I made a few changes to the game plan and a few things happened to me that made me a wiser consumer of alcohol.

The story of how *The Confusing Muse* came to be written will be revealed in Chapter Ten. As for now, one of the main takeaways is I no longer need alcohol to "approach and open" a woman. (As a preview: the upcoming chapter on Romance and Relationships discusses some of my friends. One of those characters is a police officer who has custody of his children. He also does a lot of detail work so his schedule is full. He is a user of dating "apps" and has shared some interesting stories. He has met many women in their 40s and 50s who are in a position where they don't have to work. He made the comment to me on more than one occasion that "…for many of these women, the first glass of wine happens earlier and earlier in the afternoon.")

If I think I need to have a beer at the end of the day, I now replace the beer with a bike ride or a meditation session. The meditation does two things for me that alcohol does: it slows my active brain and it also refreshes my fatigued brain (and I don't have to overhear inane bar conversations).

I look for opportunities to attend events where others are consuming alcohol and I'm not. I attend business networking events—but not as many as I once did. It's not a productive use of my time. There is almost always alcohol at these events. If I do attend one, I go to promote myself, my business and my cause. It is an odd sensation when you're in a room full of people who are consuming alcohol and you're not. The crowd gets louder and louder, many of the conversations are between people who are not replying to what each is saying but what their inebriation wants them to say. Many of the attendees go into "repeat mode" and say the same thing over and over, just at a higher volume. I'm sure bartenders understand this sensation.

I know a woman whose profession requires her to attend these types of meetings. She has to go. She ends her evening with a trip to the gym so she gets two benefits: no alcohol and a reason to leave networking events early (my opinion: she is *not* Exercise Bulimic).

Sober October

One of the world's leading sleep experts, Matthew Walker, (*Why We Sleep*), appeared on a Joe Rogan podcast. They discussed better sleep habits and Rogan also shared that he and his friends engage in "Sober October" each year. It is a month with no alcohol. I did Sober October, Sober May, and I did a Sober August. I have heard some people do a Dry January. Exactly what Matthew and Joe said would happen did happen. About the tenth day of the month, I started to experience a deep state of sleep and woke up more refreshed than normal. My dreams were vivid. I had extra time to work on various projects and was able to spend more time on my bike and devote more time to my yoga practice. I also found myself walking around with more cash than normal in my pocket. I plan to do Sober October each year and may throw in one or two more months during the year. You can watch the interview between Rogan and Dr. Walker on YouTube. If you do one Sober October (or any other month) and take advantage of the deeper sleep and extra time the alcohol-free month will provide, you will have a different relationship with alcohol going forward.

Leaving Las Vegas vs. *The Lost Weekend*

As preparation for this chapter—and because film and TV do a poor job of portraying what it is really like to consume alcohol—I revisited the 1995 movie *Leaving Las Vegas*. If you're not familiar, Nicolas Cage portrays Ben Sanderson, a failed and fired screenwriter who travels from Los Angeles to Las Vegas with a severance check and the intention of drinking himself to death. The year it was released the movie received a lot of attention, great reviews, and made a lot of noise. Cage won the Academy Award for Best Actor.

After watching the movie for a second time, my first thought was, "What were we collectively thinking in 1995?" The movie does not hold up. The story line breaks the "Chain of Plausibility" constantly, the reality of being drunk or being hungover is played as "movie hungover" and not real world hungover. And watching Nicolas Cage—with the hindsight bias of knowing what happened to him—makes it hard to take him seriously. While Elisabeth Shue didn't implode her career with this movie, she certainly detoured it.

What happened to Nicolas Cage, by the way, was making too much money—and then spending most of it on elaborate purchases. Fifteen homes, a private island in the Bahamas, castles in Germany and England, 12 Rolls-Royces, two albino king cobras (he couldn't get a puppy?) and at least one dinosaur skull. IRS liens have forced Nicolas Cage to grab any paycheck attached to a movie. The end result is that he is now responsible for some of the worst movies ever made. I haven't seen all of his straight-to-DVD efforts but one I did see that should be in the Top Ten Bad Movies of All Time: *Bad Lieutenant: Port of Call New Orleans* (2009).

I always say that a person interested in the craft of screenwriting can learn a lot from watching a bad movie, such as where the story went off the rails, when the audience stopped caring about the characters, etc. But this movie is so bad, there is nothing to be learned. It's like sitting on a train, turning to look out the window and seeing a head-on collision between two school buses loaded with children—and then having the train fall off a cliff. (Don't confuse the 2009 disaster of a movie with the much better written and acted 1992 movie *Bad Lieutenant* starring Harvey Keitel.)

I read at various times in various places that Cage had money invested with Bernie Madoff. I couldn't confirm any of those reports. But if it is true, I would imagine Nicolas Cage does not have restful, revitalizing sleep due to his financial issues. But in his jail cell, meanwhile, Bernie sleeps soundly through the night. *(Part Two of this series will deal with financial issues as one ages; Nick Cage is waiting for that book).*

If you want to watch a truly great movie that captures the grip of alcoholism 100 times better than *Leaving Las Vegas*, watch *The Lost Weekend* (1945). Directed and co-written by one of the best creators of movies ever, Billy Wilder (from a novel by Charles R. Jackson), this film gives a much more realistic sense of what it is like for a soul to be battling alcohol addiction. No hookers with a heart of gold, no fake drunk scenes and a believable story. The classic line about alcohol and alcoholics, "One's too many, and a hundred's not enough" comes from this movie. I can assure you I will not watch *Leaving Las Vegas* again but if somebody invites me to watch *The Lost Weekend*, or if a Billy Wilder Film Festival plays that movie, I will see it again and appreciate its brilliance. Lead actor Ray Milland also won the Academy Award for Best Actor for his portrayal of alcoholic Don Birnam. His performance was much more realistic than the one Nicolas Cage gave.

I've been to 24 different countries. I've had alcohol in 22 of them. In preparing this book, and after having done a few Sober Octobers, I was given the opportunity to review something that all of us who consume alcohol should do: our history and current relationship with alcohol.

CHAPTER NINE

Religion
The one and only thing we can be subjective about…

This is the second of the three chapters where I run the risk of losing audience.

In Chapter One I shared the story of my Jeep rolling across the parking lot at Caste Village. To remind: an attractive woman—three years older than me—waiting in the restaurant while I had to deal with my vehicle tapping the fender of a wrinkled, gray, aged woman one year younger than myself.

After the police left and the crowd dispersed, I returned to my date. We had much in common and enjoyed a great lunch. But it ended there. We didn't return to her nearby house for a great afternoon of fun. There was attraction and some chemistry but we parted company and I never saw her again. The reason is this: after three marriages, various boyfriends, and the constant male attention that an attractive female receives in our society, she just wanted "me" time. She was going to devote her time to her church and herself. She was not in the market for male company. At the moment she informed me of this new lifestyle, I may have had a slight bruising of my ego. But as I've gotten older and learned to appreciate and respect "me" time, I realize she was rationalizing her religious belief to help her function in this world. In other words, she was using John Lennon's line: "…whatever gets you through the night."

In Chapter Two we discussed the importance of developing an objective mind. That is essential if you want to take advantage of the benefits of writing and if you want to write something of significance. But when it comes to the subject of religion, it is the only time we can be subjective. There is no objectivity to be found in the number of different religions in this world. There is also no objectivity in the varied ways individuals have adopted different parts of their religion to arrive at the way to live their life and to come to terms with what is waiting for us on the other side.

In order for me to do this well, I need to share my religious upbringing, my insights, and my experiences. While I'm not using this chapter to convert anybody from their belief system, I am using it to state that there may be a better way to utilize religion in the aging process.

I was born to parents who were Catholic and Eastern Orthodox. My parents were married so long ago that an Orthodox person couldn't get married in a Catholic church. My parents were married in the rectory of my father's church. On the day of the wedding, my mother had to sign a document stating if she had children, they would be raised Catholic. Some years after both my parents passed away, I saw that actual document.

My father had been an altar boy at St. Adalbert's and played on the state championship basketball team for St. Casimir's. There were so many Catholic high schools back then that they had their own state-wide league. When he was a senior, my father's team won the state basketball championship in the Catholic League. On Saturday night, my brothers and I had to shine our shoes in preparation for 9:30 Mass at St. Albert's and the Sunday school that followed. I was not talented at shining shoes and always ended up with almost as much polish on my hands as on my shoes.

My brothers and I were raised Catholic but we also had exposure to my mother's religion. We celebrated Christmas on December 25th and January 7th, Easter Sunday during a different week than the Catholics (most years), and had exposure to Serbian holiday meals and traditions that my Catholic friends didn't get to experience. But while we were going to church and Sunday school with shiny shoes, we were also hearing my father talk about Nirvana. My father had been in Korea during the war. In the midst of war, he still found time to visit Buddhist temples. We were too young to fully understand the concept, but I knew it was a tenet of a religion different than my own. Maybe it was my father talking about Nirvana, or my mother's Orthodox religion mixed with my young boy's inquisitive nature, that prompted me to stand up in Sunday school and ask the teacher where the soul was in the human body. I had seen the color drawings of the human anatomy in science books and could locate the heart, lungs, kidneys, etc., but didn't know where the soul was. The teacher gave an evasive, nonsense answer about how medical science has been looking for the soul for years and years and couldn't find it. God had hidden it in our bodies. That's a good Sunday school answer—any other day of the week it wouldn't fly.

It was a different year and a different Sunday school teacher that chastised me in front of the class for turning in an essay in which I described God as my friend. I was told—along with the class—that God is definitely not my friend. He is to be feared and I better be sure not to step out of line or else there would be severe punishment.

On the street where we lived, two men—both fathers with three young children—passed away within a short period of each other. I asked yet a different teacher why God would take these men away from their families. I was told that, "God needed them. He has a special purpose for them." It seemed to me then—as now—that their young families needed them more.

Put all of that into the blender and then add the fact I attended a Catholic college where a class in theology was required. At first, I tried to get out of the requirement by telling the counselor I was Serbian. But a check of my records busted me. I was told by classmates that the Marriage class was an "easy A" (which I needed). Due to the fact I was a transfer student on academic probation, I was always the last to register. The Marriage class always booked up fast.

When I ended up in a class titled Rational Foundations of Catholic Faith, taught by Father Hogan, I didn't know what to expect. As we got underway, I realized that this class and this teacher were going to be one of the few combinations of classes and teachers that I would not only remember, but would have a lasting impact on me.

Father Hogan was the first to tell us young Catholic men and women that most of us "bought the story" because our parents did and their parents bought it before them. We weren't alone as Catholics in our thinking. We didn't have a monopoly on religion. There were other people with other beliefs who were as passionate as we were. Muslims, Jews, Baptists, Buddhists, Hindus, and others all had their belief system. It was Father Hogan who first gave me permission to think that all religion was "invented". And each inventor(s) added their own little twist to the process. Why was religion invented? According to Father Hogan it was because life was so difficult, almost impossible to survive, and there was a fear of the unknown; the other side. Something had to be created to give people a reason to survive difficult, challenging, unrewarding lives. And that was religion.

You've been with me on this journey for a while. You know I've traveled. I've seen a good bit of the world, its people, and how they lived. In Thailand I would go out of my way to visit Buddhist temples. I once went to a community of temples built by Buddhists from different countries. I asked a girl at the Nana Plaza in Bangkok to take me to her Buddhist temple. When she informed me that she was Hindu, I asked her to share with me the ideals of her belief. At the end of our day, she took me to a jewelry shop where I purchased my first AUM (or Om) symbol. This symbol, which you've most likely seen many times, is the most important symbol in Hinduism. Among other definitions, it represents the union of three gods, A for Brahma, U for Vishnu, and M for Shiva. On occasion, I wear that pendant on a chain around my neck.

Father Hogan had been "spot on" with what he told us. There was a lot going on in the world and many people had beliefs different than what I was raised with. My world vision was wide open and, once opened, it would never be shut.

I was with a beautiful girl for eight years and engaged for the last two. Her family is Baptist. I've had the experience of being in Baptist churches on many occasions. I've been to mosques and broke the Ramadan fast with shark casserole prepared by a Moroccan. I've toured some of the top museums in Europe. I've seen hundreds of paintings dedicated to the artists' religious beliefs. The artist I follow, Johannes Vermeer, has three paintings depicting religious scenes. The final Vermeer I saw, "Christ In the House of Martha and Mary" in Edinburgh, Scotland, is the largest Vermeer in terms of its size. Was Johannes making a statement with that painting about his own passion in the subject?

I understand how religion can motivate a soul to paint a painting, wage a war or build a building. In my city I used to lead bicycle tours of churches in various neighborhoods. In Homestead, there is a four-block area with 18 churches (many of them with "For Sale" signs on them). Religion has caused people to create great monuments to their belief—or start a war over those beliefs.

In Cuba, which once tried to outlaw religion, there are structures that were built hundreds of years ago. I've attended Christmas night mass at the Cathedral Basilica of Our Lady of the Assumption in Santiago, Cuba, three times. This is a church built in 1526 (not a typo) and destroyed in four different earthquakes—but rebuilt each time. Imagine the lack of tools, materials, construction techniques and the oppressive heat that was overcome to build this structure. El Cobre is a church 12 miles from Santiago. It was built to honor a statue of the Virgin Mary that two fishermen found floating in the ocean. Cubans come from across the island to this church to ask for special blessings and favors. Fidel and Raul Castro's mother supposedly put a toy soldier on the altar at the beginning of the "Revolucion" to provide her sons protection (I guess you would have to say the gesture worked). Ernest Hemingway put his Pulitzer Prize for writing *The Old Man and The Sea* on the altar as a way to give thanks. The medal was stolen (but he did get it back).

I've seen Cubans, some of the poorest, most oppressed people in the world, in church services. Their passion for their belief was almost contagious. These people have no money, no hopes of getting any, no true freedom and no hope for a better existence. But celebrate the spirit they did.

And what was Fidel thinking…trying to outlaw religion? That can't be done. Not trying to make a joke, but that would be the equivalent of the plot in the movie *Footloose* (the Kevin Bacon original; not the unnecessary remake). You can't outlaw dancing and you can't outlaw religion. People—especially those as oppressed as Cubans—require a belief system beyond what they can see in front of them just to "get them through the night".

My Belief

My unique combination of religious upbringing, travel, and exposure to religions other than the ones I started with, has delivered me to this point: I believe all religion is invented, and that people who are intense believers in their religion have never had the chance to look at other religions or have their world vision opened. I believe stories in the Bible and in the books of other religions are parables, written by the inventors of each religion to provide examples of how we should conduct our lives.

In addition to the Cubans I saw celebrating the birth of Christ, the most religious people have historically been the most oppressed. People who don't get to "spend their days" in a productive, healthy, creative way need to believe there is something on the other side to keep them going. Those who got a losing ticket in the Genetic Lottery, or spend their lives woefully underemployed often are super religious. If they weren't, what would they have to live for?

Let's say that spinal surgery I had at age 16 didn't work and I was left crippled or in severe pain with a severe limp. Add to that the two rotator cuff surgeries I've had. Imagine that there was no such thing as rotator cuff repair. So now I have two broken wings in addition to a crippled back. I had genetic cataracts and a lifelong muscle imbalance in my right eye. I've had various vision issues and surgeries. Let's say none of that was available to me. You better believe if I was a crippled man, unable to lift my arms above my head and wearing thick glasses that really didn't improve my vision, that I would be a believer. I would have to hope there was something on the other side to make up for the pain-ridden, difficult existence that was my life.

If the main reason religion was invented was to quell the fear of the other side—the unknown—then I want to share what I think happens when we take our final breath in this lifetime. But first, I want to provide insight into other aspects of religion I thought about when I outlined this chapter.

Good Use of Religion vs Bad Use of Religion

People use, or rationalize, their religion for various reasons in various ways. If a person does good deeds, is charitable, maintains a consistent manner and treats others fairly because he or she thinks "God (or their higher power of choice) is watching," then that is a good use of religion.

If a person thinks that when their tough existence here on earth, filled with pain, heartache and mostly difficult times, will be rewarded when they die and ascend into heaven and sit at the right hand of their Supreme Being, that is a bad use of religion. (Besides, that right hand would be pretty far away, even if a small fraction of the 100 billion people (100,000,000,000) who have died over the course of history are already there).

If a married couple wants to raise a family in a two-parent home full of love, support and stability because they believe God thinks that is the best way to raise children, and that couple will stay committed to each other through thick and thin (as the marriage vows state) then that is a good use of religious beliefs.

The worst use of religion I ever heard about? An acquaintance of mine survived a suicide attempt. Years later, when he told a family member about it, he was told that God puts people who attempt to take their own life right into hell. When my acquaintance replied he didn't believe in hell, he was told he would be going to "special hell" for not believing in regular hell. Not just a bad use of religion but a horrible use of it.

Religion and Mental Health

One of my uncles was a good looking, athletic person who landed at Normandy on D-Day +1. He spoke the Polish language fluently and was assigned to military intelligence in case a Polish citizen or soldier needed to be interrogated. He made appearances in six European countries. Upon returning home, he decided to hitchhike (once an acceptable form of travel) from Pittsburgh to Tennessee before looking for a job. The job he got? Flight attendant for Eastern Airlines based in New York City. With that unique beginning to life, my uncle decided to come back to Pittsburgh and get a college degree. While he was a student, something happened to him. He developed serious mental health issues. My brothers and I grew up not knowing my uncle as the guy bouncing around Europe and working as a flight attendant in the early days of aviation, but as a chain smoking, twitching, nervous man who lived with my grandparents. On more than one occasion, my uncle would stop taking his lithium and have, what my mother would call an "episode". There were times my father would have to chase my uncle down in some city neighborhood during the times he was in a manic state. My father would deliver him to the Veterans Hospital, his medication would be regulated and, after a few weeks, he would be released. He would return home to resume living with my grandparents and to his job selling hardware at Sears.

He would also return to Sunday church services at St. Bernard's Church where he sang the religious songs as loud as anyone and listened with his full attention to what the priest was saying. And he would drop more money than he could afford into the collection basket.

My uncle, and many others, had a mental illness that was magnified by religious belief. It's possible that my uncle's belief interfered with the mental health treatment he was receiving.

During one of my uncle's episodes, my parents had to deal with my grandfather in the hospital. I was in college and my father asked me to go up to the house and make sure my uncle didn't leave or hurt himself. I was a struggling student and took my textbooks and notepads in order to study. My uncle was in his bedroom but on occasion would walk up the hallway to the living room and make an announcement to me. On one of his trips, he carried up his Royal typewriter. This was an original typewriter, beautifully engineered long before the thought of electric typewriters crossed anybody's mind. The Royal had sat on the desk in my uncle's room since I could remember. He told me he was thinking of having it fixed because "…the kids were pounding on the keys and they broke it." The kids he was referring to were me and my brothers. The pounding we did happened about ten years previous. On another one of his trips up the hallway, my uncle informed me that all his problems started when he first realized that priests had to be celibate. What did that mean? Like many things said by people with mental illness, it meant something to him but nothing to anybody else.

In my quote book, I have a quote from a book written by Cyril Connelly titled *Enemies of Promise*. I associate the quote with my uncle. The quote is, "Whom the gods wish to destroy, they first call promising." My uncle had a promising beginning but mental health issues mixed with extreme religious beliefs derailed that promise.

The Other Side

What is going to happen when I die? Or when you die? The simple, direct answer is this: nothing. There are no pearly gates, no angels with wings, no reunion with those who have gone before us, looking fit and healthy. There is no playtime with that great dog you had when you were a child who ran out the door one night and never came back. When you take your last breath, that is exactly what it is: your last breath.

In the *Creed* movie, the seventh (or eighth?) film in the *Rocky* series, there is a scene where Rocky Balboa goes to the cemetery where his deceased wife Adrian is buried. He keeps a wooden folding chair in a tree. On his visits, he puts the chair in front of the headstone and talks to his dead wife. Later in the movie, Adonis Creed, after beating an Irish boxer who doesn't look like much of a boxer, goes to a different cemetery and appears in front of his father's (Apollo Creed) headstone and talks to him. Both of these conversations are only screenwriting techniques, used to convey information to the audience.

Adrian Balboa is not in the ground and neither is Apollo Creed—in fiction or in reality. My parents aren't in Mt. Lebanon Cemetery. They are within me, my brothers, and the siblings, neighbors, and friends of my parents. My parents are within me in how I conduct my life, my memories of them and in various things I've written about them. That's their afterlife. My afterlife is in the memories, the love, the inspiration and the positive works I leave behind. In the same way people reading this book are my religion, the book is part of my afterlife. *(Note: I once read that in certain parts of Africa, as long as your name is whispered you are still alive.)*

While I'm not trying to change anybody's religious upbringing or beliefs with this chapter, there is one thing that is fair to ask of you. If you are going through life with this thought in your head, "Well, I didn't get the career I wanted, didn't get the romance I wanted, didn't write the book I wanted to write, and didn't do the traveling I wanted to do BUT once I leave this earth I'll be in a better place with total happiness and fulfillment." If that's you—if that's how you're thinking—why not live your life in such a way to try to get the career you want, why not do the traveling you want, and why not write the book you want? (Chapter Two will tell you how). And, depending on your circumstances, why not try for the romance you wanted? The term "bucket list" is now common usage, thanks to the 2008 movie with Jack Nicholson and Morgan Freeman. Part of my religion is getting the items on my bucket list completed. If I happen to add an item or two as life goes on, then I've got a purpose. If you don't have a list, get one started asap.

This Is the End *(but only of this chapter…)*

As you know of me by now, I love to travel. I love preparing for trips, taking the trips, experiencing other cultures and people. But I also love coming home from trips. You also know I love movies. I have a special affinity for movies made in India. Possibly the greatest movie ever made (not just in India but anywhere) is titled *The Three*

Idiots (2007). The run time of the movie is 2 hours and 50 minutes. I've seen the subtitled version three times and the Spanish-language version once. The movie *Lagaan* has a run time of 3 hours and 44 minutes. It's about British-controlled Indians forced to pay a higher and higher percentage of their crops as a tax (lagaan) to the British military. The Indians challenge the British to a cricket game with a tax increase or decrease on the line. I won't tell you the outcome but the 3 hour and 44 minute run time flew by. I loved the movie—but I also appreciated that it had to end. I was involved in many romances but my life's great romance lasted over eight years. I appreciated it at the beginning, through most of the journey and, after it was over, I grew to appreciate it for what it was. A nice meal with healthy food, good company, excellent wine…I love that, too. But I also like when the meal is over.

Like trips, movies, and romances, this life will also one day end. It will end for me and for you and for everybody mentioned in this book—Joe Namath, Kim Novak, William Holden, Howard Stern, Bruce Springsteen, Jack Nicholson, Morgan Freeman and anybody else you can name. In Part Two of this series, we will discuss in detail estate planning, life insurance planning, living wills, life estates, and final wills. In Part Three, we will discuss End of Life issues which any enlightened society needs to improve. But for now, let's discuss a plan on how we can go out on our own terms.

If you think about it, the worst time to be a buyer of a product or service is when you absolutely need it. You will need the services of a funeral home at some point. Why not make your plans now? I knew an interesting fellow, a veteran of the USMC and director of mental health services for the county I live in. He left a 17-page detailed list of instructions for his send-off. When I showed up at the funeral home to pay my respects, the funeral home director told me my children were downstairs waiting for me. When I told the man that I didn't have children there, he was adamant that I needed to get to the basement. When I did, I was met by a bartender and a table full of Irish whiskey. It was the first time I had a shot of Jameson and also the first time I had whiskey in a funeral home.

The speakers were chosen in advance by the deceased. There was a procession from the funeral home to a local bar. We were led by a 1934 beer truck with the coffin on the flatbed. It was a long parade. The streets were lined with neighbors who probably hadn't seen this type of procession before *(I had seen such a procession once before. On the island of St. Maarten in the Dutch Indies. A cool story for another time).*

At the bar, the coffin was carried inside and set up on the stage. More Irish whiskey flowed as did cold beer—all planned and paid for by the deceased—an interesting gentleman and scholar named Chuck Peters.

Chuck may or may not have gotten the idea from Bob Fosse, the choreographer upon whose life the movie *All That Jazz* was based. Bob passed away with $10,000 in his will for his friends to throw a farewell party in his honor.

My mother, who died way too young at age 58, had a long and painful fight with a type of cancer known as liposarcoma. She knew for a long time she was going to die. I've had cousins who told me they couldn't believe how brave my mother was in her final months. One of the things she did with me was to tell me what suit and tie combinations she wanted me to wear at the two viewing sessions at the funeral home and for the funeral.

My mother was not cremated; nor was my father. But that is definitely the trend. The year 2018 marked the first year more people were cremated than buried in the traditional way. When you interfere with somebody's economic situation, they will muster a rally. And that year, in Las Vegas, it is exactly what the funeral directors did. Their trade show revealed new caskets, new limousines, new ways to prepare and present bodies, etc. Cremation, the way we should all be going out, is not a money maker for the funeral industry so that shiny new casket (or Cadillac limo, take your pick) will hopefully get family members to put their kin in the ground and help get dollars in the pockets of funeral home directors.

Do your planning in advance. That's what a responsible adult would do. One of the best exits I know of—and I have to assume it was the deceased's idea—was to write what I consider the greatest obituary ever. A gentleman named Stanley J. Kokocenski passed away in my city in 2012. His obituary read "SJK is gone." That's it. To the people who read that obit, SJK lives on.

In my quote book, I have various "last words" of famous people. While these are not his last words, these are the words of Albert Einstein leading up to the final curtain:

"I want to go when I want. It is tasteless to prolong life artificially. I have done my share; it is time to go. I will do it elegantly."

And his final words? Unknown. It turns out when Einstein died in the University Medical Center at Princeton, New Jersey, his final words were spoken in German. The nurse in the room at the time of his passing didn't know the language.

CHAPTER TEN

Romance and Relationships
("The Muse Confuses No More...")

This is the remaining chapter that may cause me to lose readers, but I hope not. It is as important as any other chapter and should be read by all ages.

The subtitle of this chapter comes from the back cover of a book I wrote under the pen name of Matthew Hawkins. The book is titled *The Confusing Muse* and is available as an eBook on Amazon. The book details the various mistakes I made in the pursuit of a fine romance and how my travels started me on the road to healthier, happier relationships. It was my intimate and numerous dealings with females in Cuba, Thailand and other ports of call that gave me the insight I needed to deal with females the best way possible in my own country.

In Chapter Three I wrote about the importance of giving up your opinions and adopting a lifestyle of objectivity. To remind: it is that objectivity that will give you to the benefits that come with living your life the way a writer lives. But when it comes to issues of the heart, it is tough for people to admit they don't know as much as they do. Most will defend their opinions just because of the subject matter. I thought I knew about love and romance for no other reason than I was a man. My ego and my pride stood in my way for a long time; until the time I got a passport and started dealing with females in other countries.

My upbringing and background will give you perception into how I used to think about the subject. My parents were married young. My aunts and uncles married young. The neighbors on our street were mostly young couples with children. I grew up on a great street (detailed in previous writings) and the small houses were close together. You couldn't help but be in your neighbors' lives. Most fathers went to work and the mothers stayed at home with the kids. This is what I saw growing up. Husband and wife working together to have a home and raise children. Divorce was a distant concept. When my godparents (also my aunt and uncle) were getting divorced, it was a somber time in our household. Back then, the newspaper printed the names of people getting divorced. My mother sat my brothers and me around the table one day, shut off the TV and dimmed the lights. She reached for the newspaper on top of the refrigerator and passed it around for us to read. It was many years ago but I still remember the shock I felt when I saw the names of my godparents in the "Divorces Filed" section of the paper.

My high school life took a dramatic detour with my back surgery and junior year spent mostly at home, but my focus was still straight: I needed to get out of school, find a job, and find somebody who would marry me. My struggles in college and being on academic probation up until two weeks from graduation didn't leave me much time for socializing. I didn't have the typical college life. I went to one fraternity party. And I was asked to leave. But I was going to find love and romance, damn it…

My extended bout with unemployment after college didn't help matters but I stayed on track, even though the train was late leaving the station. On occasion, I attended church service at St. Albert's. In the bulletin there was a section called "Bands of Marriage". If you were going to be married in the church, you had to attend three classes with the priest. Each week, the names of each engaged couple would be printed along with the number of classes they completed. That was the first section I looked at in the bulletin. When I saw the name of a girl I knew, I would have to mentally take her off the Rolodex in my mind as potential marriage material. When I saw the names of certain guys I knew, I would think to myself, "How the hell did he find somebody to marry him?" Marriage was on my mind. I needed to get a job and find somebody to marry me.

When I started working, things changed for me, but not in the way I thought they would.

I was a young man in an era of large nightclubs, less than strict drinking and driving laws, and willing females sitting on barstools. I was going to find my wife but—in the interim—why not have some fun? I developed a strong physique from swimming, grew into my broken nose, drove a jet-black Camaro Z-28 and I had a certain "lounge lizard" appeal. It also helped me that I fit in at any bar or club I went to, from the upscale clubs downtown to the flannel and jeans bars in the South Hills. I could talk to females. But, to be honest, much of my "success" had to do with the fact I went out often, went out late, and had great staying power. Right place, right time was my ticket on many nights.

As I reached my mid- to upper 20s, I was getting more involved with my writing projects. At some point, I became aware of the concept of the Muse. In Greek mythology, there are sisters (some accounts say three, others say nine), all beautiful, whose main purpose was to provide inspiration and motivation to the painters, sculptors, and writers of the day. The word "music" can be traced back to the Greek word "mousa". There is a word for the "…place where Muses are to be worshipped." You know that word as "museum".

I started looking for my Muse. I was going to find a female who would provide me the inspiration to create, achieve and accomplish. I would marry a Muse, have a great house, spend my Saturdays working on writing projects before going out to dinner with my Muse and then returning home for a great night of romance. We would have a great life, a great family, a great home, and we would support each other.

How was I going to meet this Muse? Simple. It would be just like the movies. I would meet my Muse the same way Montgomery Clift met Elizabeth Taylor in *A Place in the Sun*, the way William Holden met Kim Novak in *Picnic,* and the same way Gary Cooper gave Patricia Neal the once over twice in *The Fountainhead* before embarking on an intense romance. I would be somewhere and she would be there. Our eyes would meet and that would be the beginning of my fine romance. Not familiar with the movies I cited? How about the song "Some Enchanted Evening"? My Muse and I would be multi-media. As you read the following lyrics, imagine Frank Sinatra and Keely Smith singing them as a duet:

> Some enchanted evening
> You may see a stranger
> You may see a stranger
> Across a crowded room
> And somehow you know
> You know even then
> That somewhere you'll see her
> Again and again

Some enchanted evening
Someone may be laughin'
You may hear her laughin'
Across a crowded room
And night after night
As strange as it seems
The sound of her laughter
Will sing in your dreams

Who can explain it?
Who can tell you why?
Fools give you reasons
Wise men never try
> -Rogers and Hammerstein
> from *South Pacific*

I did meet more than a few Muses. Just like the song lyrics, I
would see an attractive female across a crowded room. My crowded
room was usually a bar or a nightclub but there were "non-bar"
Muses also. I saw one of my Muses showing off her new car to her
friends before meeting her. I saw another Muse for the first time
taking out her garbage before meeting her in the neighborhood bar.

But ideas are one thing and reality is another. Instead of my
Muses making me a happy, focused, creative person, and instead of
the subject of my affection and me being in a great romance, it was
the exact opposite. My girls had jobs that they didn't care for (not
spending their days well) and I was Mr. Ambition talking about
writing projects, movies, and business ideas. They really didn't want
to hear that. The few great times I had with these physically
attractive females where I felt like I was on the road to something—a
fine romance—were greatly outnumbered by the times when I had
doubt, lack of confidence and a heavy heart. I was dealing from a
position of weakness. I let these females lay down "eggshells". This
is a term used for subjects I would be afraid to bring up because my
Muse's reaction wouldn't bode well for me. Many phone calls ended
with me analyzing the details of the call. "What did she mean by
that?" "Why didn't she want to see me this weekend?" "Did she
really have to get off that phone that fast?" "Are cordless phones
really dangerous during a storm?" All of this self-doubt and

questioning was tempered with a big lie that I would keep telling myself: "Ken, you have to go through these hard times to end up with your life's great romance."

I never arrived at that great romance. If these females were interested in romance, it wasn't with me. Any involvement I had with a Muse ended poorly—for me. You would think I would have learned something from my first or second or fifth heartbreak but I didn't. I stayed in "Muse mode" for a long time before gaining the insight I needed to carry on. And where did that insight come from? One word: Cuba. No, two words. Cuba and Thailand.

A passport is a great asset. I got one and had dozens of amazing experiences in Cuba, Thailand, Hong Kong, et. al., with beautiful women. The experiences gave me the insight needed to correct the mistakes I had been making in pursuit of romance. When I returned home after each trip, I noticed I was dealing with females in a different manner. I was no longer interested in explaining Greek mythology to attractive females *(ever try to explain the concept of the Muse to a blonde stripper? I did.)* I came to two realizations: (1) if I was going to be a creative person I would be so because I wanted to share my experiences and insights, and not because I would need an attractive female to inspire me and (2) the concept of the Muse is a great romantic device for novels and movies—but it is not the real world. You can read about my unique experiences in Cuba in *Under a Cuban Sky* and my epiphany into the ways of the Muse in *The Confusing Muse*. The former is a printed book and the latter is in eBook format, both on Amazon.

As with many things in life, there are relevant quotes to share and learn from. Here are a few quotes I wish I had read before I went down the wrong road with my flawed thinking about romance:

> "What a strange illusion it is to suppose that beauty is goodness!"
>
> ---Leo Tolstoy
> (from *Anna Karenina*)*

This quote is self-explanatory. I gave physically attractive females—females who held winning tickets in the Genetic Lottery— character traits that they just didn't have. And that was my problem, not theirs. In life, persistence is a good trait to have—for most things. But I was persistent for all the wrong reasons. One of my Muses, in particular, not only kept throwing up red flags warning me to stay away from her but she took the pointy end of the flag pole, stuck it in my eye socket and twisted it around. I persistently, and foolishly, thought it was all just part of the journey to a great romance. And I was wrong.

*Tolstoy's complete quote: "What a strange illusion it is to suppose that beauty is goodness! A beautiful woman utters absurdities; we listen, and we hear not the absurdities but wise thoughts." *A list of idiotic things physically attractive women said to me that I did not challenge would be the fourth book in this series.*

"Nobody can bring you happiness but yourself."
--Ralph Waldo Emerson

There were times I told myself, "I won't be happy, really happy, unless I end up with _____ (*fill in the name of any Muse*). But it was my travels and my experiences in other countries that made me realize happiness wasn't going to arrive at my door presented to me by a female. Happiness is a combination of things: acceptance of yourself by yourself, how you are spending your days, having a point to your life, the ability to create, your health, physical activity, etc. For a long time, I erroneously thought that my "one-itis" thinking about a specific female was the only thing that would make me happy. And I was wrong.

"The one that cares the least controls the relationship."
--Anonymous

I learned of this quote while writing TCM. I've been on both sides of this fence. As for my Muses, I cared about them a whole lot more than they cared about me. I thought my persistence, charm and creativity would equal out the playing field. And I was really wrong.

"Most of us love from our need to love, not because we found someone deserving."
--Nikki Giovanni**

True. True. True. Guilty. Guilty. Guilty *(at least until I got my passport)*.

** Nikki Giovanni is a poet and educator. She wrote the ultimate biography of The Isley Brothers for their CD compilation set.

The Age(s) of Romance

Before getting into the heart of this chapter, let me reintroduce myself. I am a heterosexual male. I am not married and never have been. I was with the same girl for eight years and—like the joke goes—happy for seven and one half of them. Our engagement lasted two years. It was my life's great romance. I will also state that I've had a lot of experience with members of the opposite sex. What you read from this point to the end of the chapter is written from that perspective.

Some of us will be in long-term, happy, committed marriages. Some of us will be divorced or lose a spouse late in life, through divorce or death. I have no idea what either is like and no matter what somebody in either situation tells me, I could never fully appreciate those experiences. When people ask me what it's like to be in Cuba, I tell them my words can't explain it. I've written about Cuba and they can read my books and essays, but that doesn't even begin to share the actual experience. If you've never written a book, I can't explain to you what it is like to spend months writing on note cards and legal pads and then sitting in front of a computer screen for even more months doing the actual writing. You have to experience it for yourself. However, on my behalf and in my defense, I was in a long-term relationship. I know about moving from intense physical attraction to a combined physical and mental attraction. I know sharing intimate secrets with one person and silly debates such as who was the first to say "I love you." I know about waking up next to the same person for a long time, I know about "What's for dinner?" and I know about "Where should we go on vacation?" I know about holiday gatherings and I know about driving a young child to the ER in the middle of the night. I know about going to school events and seeing the excitement in a young child in the weeks leading up to Christmas. I know about buying an engagement ring and, unfortunately, I know about selling an engagement ring. Nobody is more qualified to write what you're about to read than I am.

The romantic life of some of us will be limited to the memories of past romances and encounters. That segment of the population will surf those memories to the end. Some of us will be more interested in companionship than passion. Some of us will be interested in dating only around the end of the year. That segment will want to have a "plus one" to attend holiday parties and family gatherings with *(a friend once proposed the Holiday Matchmaking Service—you are matched with somebody the night before Thanksgiving, date through the holidays, and break up the day after Valentine's Day).*

But some of us will continue to try to meet new people, "advance our cause" and get ourselves into romantic interludes. I can certainly comment on that. And although I'm a man, there will be things in this section and in the end of the chapter that will benefit both sexes—regardless if they're in a long-term relationship or in search of a romance.

When TCM was released, I received a not-too-friendly email from a woman who ran a dating service in Pittsburgh called "The Green Band Club". The mission of the club was as silly as the name implies. Members would wear a green wrist band when they were at social events. If you saw a person with such a band, you knew they were in the club and available for dating. The purpose was to make the "approach and open" a bit easier. The email sent to me took exception to the way I used the terms "female" and "woman" in my book. I was scolded via email that I used the terms incorrectly. An article was attached explaining when to use "female" and when to use "woman". That email and article were deleted faster than the Green Band Dating Club lasted. If I use the term "woman" or "female" incorrectly, I'm asking you to forgive me in advance. I will also ask for forgiveness if I use the term "girl" in describing a female younger than myself or a female I went to high school with (they will always be girls to me because they were around me during the day and in my head at night as my libido was being developed).

I graduated from high school with 971 other people. To the best of my knowledge, there were at least 10 marriages from people who met in my school, dated, and got married. Only one that I know of ended in a divorce. I think there is something incredibly sweet about meeting young, marrying young, growing together—through good times and bad—and raising a family.

That is the way I was brought up to believe things should work. It didn't work for me but it worked for some of my high school classmates. I had absolutely nothing to do with any of these people meeting, dating or getting married, but I carry a certain amount of pride just because I attended school with those involved.

<u>Bumper Cars</u>

When you reach a certain point in life and you are looking for romance, the process will be like the amusement park staple—bumper cars. Your lifestyle is set, your views of the world are set, your habits are set. You are out in the world with people in the same situation. Everybody has had past romances and past relationships. These will impact potential future romantic entanglements. These may impact (most likely negatively) how you "bump". You then set off in your bumper car hoping to bump into somebody with the similar views, lifestyles and direction as you. You are looking for mutual physical attraction and chemistry that can be heightened by mental attraction. You are also looking for somebody whose company you want to be in—and can stand being in for long periods of time (easier written than done).

Since I wrote TCM, online dating has become a bigger part of society for all age groups. I'm sure there are 20-year-olds thinking they are cool using Tinder to swipe left and right. They may lower Tinder on the cool scale if they knew how many people in their 60s and 70s were using that same dating app (short for "application"). I will write in detail about online dating later in this chapter. As for now, I will write for male readers and then female readers.

<u>"Approach and Open"</u>

While online dating is now an accepted part of meeting partners for all ages, I'm of the school of thought that we still need to be working on our in-person meeting skills. And the one thing that men must start doing more of is "approaching and opening". When you see a person you find attractive and may be interested in, start a conversation. Don't think that some pre-planned, rehearsed opening line is required. "Hello" works great or a simple comment about where you are, what is happening around you, etc. It is not the content that matters; it is the way you present it. Most likely you will be a bit nervous on the "open" so keep your words short and to the point. But you must say something. Talk to the people you find attractive. You're there, she's there and you're in the batter's box. Get the bat off your shoulder.

One of the best forms of cheap entertainment is found on Craigslist under the section "Missed Connections". It is full of messages posted by men (never women) who saw a female in the supermarket or some other public place. Instead of talking to them, the men hurry home to their computer and post a message. The messages will say something like, "Saw you in the supermarket. I wanted to say 'hi' but you looked too busy. If you see this, send me a message." Or, "You were getting gas. I was next to you. Did we have a moment at the gas pump? Write to me and tell me what color car I have." I doubt that in the history of Craigslist, any of these posts have been responded to. A woman likes a man who knows what he's doing and that includes having the ability to approach and open. There are certain items that make for a successful Approach and Open.

Study for Your Test

Cold hard fact of life: when you do a successful "approach and open" you will most likely be met with resistance. Females approached by a male will almost automatically block any opening, even if done in an innocent, non-threatening way. Guys will back down at that point but men know what to do. They have to come back with their second open. Expect your nervously-delivered open to be defended. Be ready with your backup. I know a fellow who manages a parking garage for a hospital. He is a nice-looking guy, certainly no Dash Riprock but good looking enough, and he has a good sense of humor. A girl (sorry, Green Band Club) who works in the hospital used the garage. He talked to her for months when she was coming through the garage. He thought he had gotten to the point to invite her out. One morning, he suggested they go for coffee. She immediately replied, "No, thank you." Quicker than her rejection, he said, "Well, then, how about some tea?" She laughed and accepted the invite. At last report, they have been happily married for two years.

The Eyes Have It—Part One

Of super importance: it's imperative to make and maintain eye contact upon meeting. It is not easy but it must be done. It should be practiced with everybody you interact with, romantic intention or not. There is a proper way to "talk" with your eyes. You don't need to keep contact 100% of the time; that would fall under the definition of creepy. A study I referenced in TCM stated the amount of time you should have eye contact in conversation is 91%. When looking into somebody's eyes, mix up your contact. Look into both of their eyes, then put both of your eyes into one of their eyes. Look away when you are searching for a word. If the person on the other side of the conversation has studied the art and science of conversation, they know that when your eyes dart up to your left, that what you're saying is not the truth or it is an embellishment of the truth. If your eyes dart up to your right, they know you are deep in thought and really thinking about what you're about to say. When you start talking with somebody, make a mental note immediately as to what color their eyes are.

The "I's" Have It—Part Two

In sixth grade, my teacher was Mr. McMillian. He was the first male teacher I had, he had been on the swim team at Thiel College and he drove a Ford Falcon. He was one of the few teachers who left a lasting influence on me, like Father Hogan at Duquesne University (but in a much different way). Mr. McMillian told the class a story about a party he attended. When walking in to the party, he was given a badge with the letter "I" on it. There was a contest unfolding. How long could you go without using the word "I" in a sentence? If you spoke to somebody who used "I" in a sentence, you got their badge. If you lost your badge, you had to trip somebody else up to take their badge. Whoever collected the most badges at the end of the evening received a prize (maybe the prize was that sweet Ford Falcon).

Mr. McMillian's story has always stuck with me. In having a conversation, you should speak half as much as you listen. You must be careful not to talk about yourself too much. In conversation, imagine you're wearing the "I" badge and you don't want to give it away. This will be difficult for many people. There is a large percentage of the population who think they are more interesting than they really are. They think the rest of the world wants to hear their stories and their opinions. You know my travel history and things I've been involved with. Guess what? To many of the people in my city, especially those who haven't been out of the city except on a few occasions, I'm a boring person. Like my creative soul, once I acknowledged my boring persona, most aspects of my life improved.

Proper Way to Compliment

Attractive females receive compliments nonstop. In early conversation, this could implode your chances of "advancing your cause". Attractive women know they are attractive. If you're going to pay a female a compliment early in conversation, make the compliment about something she had to use her brain to achieve. Compliment her on her choice of shoes or boots, her purse, a piece of jewelry. Do not compliment her on something she had nothing to do with—her appearance. Females know this and overhear it. If you do compliment a woman on her looks, she will mark you as a man—or guy—who doesn't know what he is doing.

Beware of the Dreaded Thread

In the world of "meeting," the word "thread" refers to the direction and tone of the initial conversation. Most threads go nowhere and are pointless. Most threads are the same old over and over: Where are you from? What do you do? What spots do you go to? Most of the people you speak with have been doing this for years (if not decades) and they are fine with pointless threads. If you are trying to advance your cause, you have to detour from the thread and go your own way. While avoiding the thread, remember to keep the "I"s (and the alcohol) to a minimum.

What the heck is GU?

GU is an abbreviation for a phrase that has more importance the older you get. It stands for Geographically Undesirable. In my ballroom days, I dealt with females in far away small towns such as Delmont, Grindstone, Perryopolis and West Newton. As one gets older, and as their time is compressed, it matters where people you are interested in dating call home. A few 50-mile road trips to be a gentleman caller may be doable at first but the older you are, the faster it gets played out.

The Rules of Attraction

The Italian poet Dante said, "Love enters through the eyes." He was saying we are attracted to who and what we are attracted to. We could develop our attractions when our libidos are being developed. We could see a female, a photo of a female, or a movie with a female in it that registers with us. It is a fact of life that must be accepted. You may be attracted to somebody who is just not into you. I used to think I could make somebody attracted to me through my ambition, creativity and charming personality. But now I know that if a female doesn't like the package those attributes are wrapped in, there is no point being persistent. What you just read took me only seconds to write but years to learn.

Another way of sharing this insight is to make sure you don't mistake interest or politeness for attraction. A female may be interested in your career as a skydiving plumber who performs open heart surgery on puppies with heart conditions in your spare time. But that doesn't make her attracted to you.

Contact Information

If you have done a fine job of approaching and opening and have advanced your cause, depending on the location and circumstance, you may ask the object of your affection for a phone number, a business card or try to set up a day, time, and place to meet. We now have Facebook pages, email addresses, etc. When I used to ask for a woman's phone number and they asked for mine instead, I would say, "That's OK. It's not that important." I didn't use business cards until recently. I now have a card with information about one of my books and two YouTube videos. I have no issue giving that card to females.

One can obtain cards from females in business or social events. The cards are usually given by a female thinking you may be a business connection. One must tread lightly in trying to turn that into a romantic connection. Most individuals now have email addresses or social media pages easily accessible. This is a way to express an interest in somebody using today's technology. But be careful. There is a fine line between being a persistent suitor and an annoying pest. Don't cross that line.

I came up before there was Caller ID on phones. You could call a female, get an answering machine and hang up. Now, if you make that call, you're probably going to get voicemail. Be ready. Don't "um" and "ah" through your message. Sweet, succinct, and to the point. You may also text for your first contact. Don't do the "Hey" open. Share who you are and ask a question—but anything other than "Want to get together?" If you get no reply—and you should plan on that—call or text two more times, with days in between. If no reply, move along. You may see that person again and you'll have an easier time to "approach and re-open".

For the Ladies

As most of this section was for men still interested in pursuing a fine romance, it was written from that standpoint. In TCM there is a chapter written for the benefit of women. The summary of that chapter is as follows: men are usually nervous in approaching women. Even if we don't show it, there is a bit of nervousness involved. The typical woman is turned off by nervousness, but I think it is important for a female to know that we won't always be nervous. Under that mangled approach and opening could be a stable, fun, consistent man with a good heart. So, to the ladies reading this, we won't always be nervous. And at the risk of contradicting Dante's famous quote (and fighting human behavior), I am going to do just that. If you're the woman who tells yourself and your friends that you're only attracted to men who are 6'5" inches tall and wear suits and ties each day, expand your horizons. Maybe the 5'9" man who wears suits only on occasion has other qualities and attributes that make up for his lack of height. Open your eyes and broaden your horizons. It may lead to a better romance than you've had in the past.

<u>"Profiles" in Online Dating</u>

The above title is taken from Chapter Nine in TCM. Online dating is bigger than it was when I wrote TCM. Once again, I am going to write this section from the standpoint of a man interested in meeting a woman with notes for women at the end. And, once you learn of an interesting Match.com experience I had, you'll understand why my end notes are longer than in the previous section.

I've had a lot of great romances with online meetings. The site that I used is no longer operational. I now rely on stories from friends who use dating sites to keep me up to date on the online dating world. But my Match.com experience gave me insight and inside knowledge that no friend could ever acquire and share.

What happened to me was exactly what happened to Cyrano de Bergerac. If you don't know the character or the play, Cyrano was a talented, articulate man who pulled a losing ticket in the Genetic Lottery. He had a huge nose which defined his appearance. His distant cousin Roxane was a beautiful girl who had many male suitors—Cyrano among them. Also vying for Roxane's attention was Christian, the handsome man. Cyrano wrote a letter to Roxane expressing his love but allowed Christian to take credit for the letter. Cyrano also "fed" the words for Christian to say to Roxane as he courted her affections.

The modern day "Cyrano" started with a phone call from a friend. He put up seven photos of himself working out in his home gym on a Match.com profile. He wanted me to write his profile and then to start sending messages to females he was interested in. He ran a successful construction business but had zero writing ability.

I jumped into this assignment. I wrote a profile that was accurate in detailing my friend. He was interested in dating but his business and personality worked best when he had a lot of time by himself (similar to myself). When the profile went up, my friend and I would spend time on the phone at night. We would both be on his Match profile, and he would tell me which females to contact.

It was a great learning experience and gave me much insight. The experience is detailed in the TCM. The highlights from reading numerous female ads: six out of ten females like to "…dine in, dine out, walk on the beach and cuddle on the couch during the Steelers game." *The beach thing got to me because there is no beach in my city.* Many females had user names that are derived from the local sports teams:

SteelersGal101, PensGal101, SteelersPensGal101—and numerous other combinations. One of the most repeated phrases to start a profile was "My friends would describe me as…." Too many of the profiles showed photos of the profile owner with female friends in a bar drinking alcohol. Some of the women felt it was OK to post photos of their pets (good idea) and their children (really bad idea).

This experiment went on for three months. When I replied to a woman, I replied with a question about something in her profile or one of the photos. I ended my reply with a question.

Now, many of the females I reviewed wrote how important good communication was in a relationship (which I agree with). But when I replied with a well written message, and asked a direct question, the ones that did reply did so with a five-word answer and many times didn't answer the question I asked. So, while communication is important, according to their post, it wasn't that important when replying to me (or to the photos of my friend!).

At the time, Match.com had a filter where you selected various search factors. Age range, distance from your ZIP Code, body type, ethnicity, etc. There was also a criterion for income level. When my friend and I entered our age ranges and "non-smoking" we would have 800 profiles within a 20-mile radius. When we chose income level above $50,000, the 800 was reduced to 175 profiles. Keep in mind, the income figure was self-reported by the female.

One night, I received a call from my friend. There was a woman whose ad he wanted me to see and then reply to. It turns out the posting belonged to one of my Muses. She had posted 26 photos of herself. I hadn't been in her house for over ten years but some of the photos I saw in her house were on her post—with the faces of past boyfriends crossed out, of course. He knew my history with this female. I told her she didn't post in search of romance; she just wanted many people to gaze at her photos. We didn't write to her but within one year I wrote about her in TCM.

I ended up meeting two of the females we corresponded with. The perfect lives they painted online weren't so perfect in real life. A female I wanted to meet but didn't worked as a legal secretary. She and I had great correspondence. For a few weeks we had Saturday at 6:00 p.m. instant messenger dates. At one point my friend called to let me know this woman had posted a full-length photo of herself. I thought that she did it for me—or for me and my friend.

When I revealed to her, as I did the others, that each word she read was mine but the photos weren't of me, she replied in all capital letters—which I knew wasn't good. She threatened legal action and vowed to have my friend's Match.com membership suspended. My time on Match.com ended shortly thereafter. On an ironic note, a few years later I was at an event and met the legal secretary. I didn't tell her I knew her from past correspondence. She was an attractive woman but I had no interest in her once I met her.

If you do (or are doing) online dating, there is something you should know. You may be on Match.com and then try Plenty of Fish and then jump to OurTime or Senior Match. Do not be the least bit surprised if you find the same people circulating on these sites.

Early Stages of Romance

You've met somebody. It doesn't matter how. It could have been online, through a family introduction, walking down the street, in the supermarket or through a matchmaker (I would be so great in that profession). Many great romances never happen because of mistakes made early on. I've made them and shared them in TCM, Chapter Twelve. For this book, I will summarize five of the Top Seven Mistakes made in the early stages of romance. Read them, learn them, live them (paraphrased from *Fast Times at Ridgemont High*). While these are written from the vantage point of a man, all five apply to females.

(1) Too clingy

I appreciate the fact you've met somebody you're interested in. But too many calls, texts, and emails will hurt you early on and not help you. Absence does make the heart grow fonder. No need to send multiple messages and make phone calls each day. Don't act like a puppy constantly looking for attention from somebody you've just met. It will not "advance your cause," it will derail it. Clingy = needy.

(2) Too quick to return messages

Unfortunately, the testing continues. You've met somebody and spent time with them. They call. You answer. They start a thread and you go along with it. The person on the other end of that phone will grow tired of you if you are too quick to answer the phone or return a message. Mix things up. Answer some of those calls right away, return some of those calls an hour later, and return other calls the next day. In today's world of communications, we can answer phone calls with a pre-populated text message: "Sorry, can't talk now," or "I'll call you later." Or make up your own text to reply to a call.

(3) <u>We let eggshells develop</u>

Many of us will go out of our way to avoid confrontation. We are allergic to it. When I was dealing with my Muses, there were topics I knew to avoid because I would be given the old "freeze out". These topics were like eggshells. Once I let those eggshells be established, they were like beachheads. They weren't going to be removed. Those "eggshell-creating" topics were always there in the background and caused a permanent, ever-so-slight uneasy feeling in my heart. Going forward, don't let early romance issues become eggshells. If a woman—or man—doesn't appreciate you standing up to them, they're not worth your time and attention.

(4) <u>We overbuy presents</u>

This doesn't seem like a big deal but it is. Early in a romance, if you buy a present that is too expensive or too personal, it could come off as if you're trying to buy affection. If it's lingerie or something similar, and you're not at that level, it's going to be way out of line. A woman equates the overbuying of presents with a man who doesn't know what he's doing. Be creative with your gift buying if Christmas, Valentine's Day, or your (hopefully) new romance's birthday occurs shortly after you have met. The item and the price point do matter.

(5) <u>We fight the physical compatibility tape</u>

Initial physical attraction can (some will say most of the time it will) fade away. Some of us, in pursuit of a great romance, will continue seeing that person. But why? Attraction, per Dante, is the basis of a romance. I've met females I was attracted to at first but, after a few dates and seeing them in different situations and stages of dress, lost that attraction. So, why fight the tape? It's doubtful any of those females would turn around and become attractive to me. And this will go against you as well. A person you meet who is physically attracted to you at first may lose that attraction. No guarantee that initial attraction will become permanent. It's not a good thing or a bad thing. It's just the way things are. I would be dishonest this late in the book if I said it didn't happen to me. It's happened many times.

The News Rules of Romance

With this book, I'm announcing New Rules of Romance. Let's treat each other better in our pursuit of romance, be it in person or online. Let's not make every first meeting centered around alcohol. Museums and galleries are cool places for first meetings. And during that first meeting, why not be "technology free"? Put your phones away. Talk to the person you've agreed to meet. If there is no chemistry, you can survive a 20-minute meeting without checking your phone every few minutes. Speaking of phones, my dating app friend told me about meeting a woman through a site called Bumble. They met in a bar/restaurant and sat at a table.

They spoke for a few moments and he went to the bar to get drinks. On his way back to the table, the woman was seated with her back to him. As he approached, he could look over her shoulder. She was on her phone looking at other profiles on the dating site they met on. That doesn't work under the New Rules of Romance.

That same friend has told stories about meeting women who have alcohol and ex-husband issues—and they have no issue exhibiting one while talking about the other. That friend met an online date at a local bar. She told her friends where she was going. Her friends, also no strangers to alcohol, showed up. A meeting between a man and woman to see if there was chemistry ended up as a drinking festival.

Why don't we make our online profiles more accurate? If you are writing about your perfect life in an online profile, it's not so perfect. And how about a rule stating that photos used in dating profiles have to have been taken in the current decade?

I think just the realization at a certain age we're "bumper cars" will go a long way to making better connections. It is hard for some females to appreciate that my weekends aren't centered around restaurants, alcohol and sports on TV. My life is my life. Your life is your life. It is not everybody else's. Be open to that.

For the men: you need to write better online profiles and improve your correspondence game. Many of my positive online adventures are a direct result of my ability to write and not because I'm such a good-looking guy (which I'm not!). This is another reason for you to start living your life the way a writer does. And, if you're out in public and see a woman you're attracted to, don't run home to post in Missed Connections on Craigslist. "Approach and open." Make and keep proper eye contact. And do so knowing you're probably going to be met with a Wall of Defense (new term just invented) at first. You have to come back with your second volley. You've got to get over that Wall (an anonymous quote I have to use here: "Women with the highest walls give the deepest love").

For the women: when a nervous guy approaches you, realize he's a nervous guy approaching you. You don't like the way he looks? Not attracted to him? That's fine. At least give him the chance to get better at "approaching and opening". Let him get into his second open (for lack of a better term). You can share your lack of interest in a polite, diplomatic way. And don't take contact information unless you're going to use it.

For both sexes: if you do meet somebody and the bumper cars seem to be going in the same direction, that's great. But if they veer off, don't just stop dealing with the other person. Don't just stop responding to calls, texts or emails. Call them and let them know you appreciated meeting them but there isn't mutual chemistry. I've been on both sides of that call. If you're a man and get that call, don't be a whiner. Buck up and move on. It's a wonderful thing when there is mutual physical and mental attraction on the part of two people. It's rare. If it happened all the time it wouldn't be so wonderful.

Let's treat each other with respect and openness and the appreciation that it is a natural, healthy, important thing to be interested in romance. You may not have—or lose—romantic interest in another. But there is no need for lies, deceit, or the hurting of feelings.

<u>Final Thoughts (for this chapter)</u>

I promised something of value that would benefit people in all stages of romance, even those in multi-decade long marriages. And I will keep that promise. But first, I want to share other thoughts that developed while writing this extremely important chapter.

I've not been in a long-term marriage. I already provided that news. But it dawned on me that meeting somebody, falling in love, deciding to get married, and staying married for many years is a little analogous to writing a book. The writer gets the spark of an idea (meets somebody), thinks about that idea and develops related ideas for more depth (initial dates), then gets serious about the project (engagement). The writer's passion for the book propels him to write an outline and do the necessary research (getting married). The writing usually starts off strong (early days of marriage) but then slows down (married couple settling into life). There is progress made in spurts (happily married) but the writer's block eventually rolls in (stormy seas of marriage). The writer then has to return to the outline to make sure it was structured properly and then re-read what has been written to this point.

There will be a time—maybe multiple times—where the writer has a thought of tossing the whole thing aside and going onto a different project (I'm sure most couples, at some point, have that thought about their marriage). Then the writer realizes the outline is strong, what has been written to this point is good and that their passion for the project is still strong (as couples truly in love do). Until the end of the project (marriage) there will be good writing days that hopefully outweigh the bad writing days. And there will be a point reached where the writer knows they will finish the project (the same way a couple settles in to their marriage with many, many more happy memories than not so happy ones).

I realize how lucky I was for my parents to reach the point where they realized they *wanted* to be parents. They signed on for whining kids, fighting among their sons, driving kids to Little League games, and making sure every birthday and Christmas were great events, regardless of life challenges that were going on at the time. They never complained while taking their three sons to various doctors, hospitals, or specialists. Whatever was needed, they did it. And my brothers and I are better for it. I have relatives and friends who were great back in their ballroom days. They had fun being young and single. But I see them now as older married individuals with children. And those children (and grandchildren) are lucky because these friends and cousins also got to the point when they decided that they *wanted* to be parents.

Before I share the one single character trait that both halves of a couple must have, one last story. Years ago, before I entered the investment industry and got involved with the nutrition and fitness industries, I had a job with the U.S. Census Bureau. It was in Clairton, PA. Depressed town. No police force. Low-income. High crime. The only reason I got the job was that nobody wanted to go into Clairton with no protection except for a U.S. Census Taker badge (which many mistook for a parole officer's badge). My job was to "enumerate" households who hadn't returned the form mailed to their house. It didn't take me long to realize why other people didn't want the job. I didn't know the neighborhood. If I had, I probably would have waved off on the job. But I had taken the job and any job you're getting paid to do is worth doing well.

I was around Clairton for a few months. One day, I went to an address where a couple in their early 60s lived. They welcomed me into their nicely-kept home and told me they hadn't received anything from the Office of the Census. They were glad to answer my questions. We sat in the living room and I started to ask the list of questions on my script. One of the first questions dealt with length of time at their current address.

In a quiet voice, the wife answered, "Since 1968."

In a move that surprised me, the husband turned and almost took her head off.

"You don't know what the hell you're talking about!! We got here in 1967! What the hell is the matter with you?!"

I was embarrassed for the wife. She sat there with a forced smile on her face. She didn't react to her husband's attack. Something told me this wasn't the first time this happened.

When I asked another question, it was a similar replay. The wife answered and the husband "corrected" her answer in a loud voice. She sat there looking at me. I know she was embarrassed but she put on a forced smile and took the abuse.

Now, the couple probably stayed married until one of them died. But they shouldn't have. It was an abusive relationship. Maybe not physical but certainly verbal. I'm sure that woman had no job skills and was tied to that marriage and that A-Hole of a husband. She was an economic prisoner in that marriage. There are many others like that. Many females have stayed married because they couldn't get out. And even though income inequality among the sexes is still high (average woman earns 70 cents per each dollar the average man earns), I am glad that more women now have the ability to "get out" when they should.

One more thought before my great insight. I went from being they guy who would do everything to avoid arguments with romantic partners—tiptoe around the eggshells—to being the man that argued the wrong way. I had disagreements that turned into arguments with the girl I was with for eight years. She raised her voice and I followed. She said mean-spirited things and I followed suit. I really loved this woman but the times we argued were out of control. Any solid relationship will have disagreements. If there weren't any disagreements that means one of the parties cares less about the relationship than the other party and is "driving the bus". The passenger is doing what I did for many years—anything to avoid confrontation.

A disagreement should be talked about, not YELLED about. Don't use any language that could be construed as offensive. Don't practice "transference," the concept of bringing something lingering in in the background into the disagreement currently on the table. Today's disagreement is today's disagreement. It is normal to love somebody and to have disagreements with them. And, although I have no empirical experience, I have to imagine most couples who are together for decades see a decline in their disagreements the longer they are married (all except for that couple in Clairton, PA).

Here is the great insight. It came to me as I was finishing up TCM. Early in the book I wrote that the number one criterion for establishing a relationship was physical attraction. And I stand by that statement although I know there are other reasons people get together, especially as they get older, such as companionship or financial stability.

But, without a doubt, the main character trait people must have in order to be in happy and healthy romances is **consistency**. We must be consistent in our dealings with our spouses, girlfriends, boyfriends and all the way down to the people we are meeting for the first time on a dating site or in person. Don't be overly attentive and caring one day and cold and distant the next. Be the same person in the morning as in the evening. Be consistent in your disagreements. You'll have them, but be the same person at the beginning of the disagreement as at the conclusion. The art of consistency should carry over to anybody you deal with: friends, co-workers, employers, employees, the people whose names you don't know but say "hi" to on the street.

That is the end of the heart of this book. In Chapter Two I wrote that writing is a cathartic endeavor. I listed it as one of the reasons you should live your life the way a writer does. I didn't realize until I was halfway through the first draft of the manuscript how powerful that catharsis was. The planning and writing of this book provided me benefits I hadn't thought about during the outline process. As an older individual I am now even more focused on the things I want to accomplish, and more open to technology and change, and more appreciate of my time—and yours.

As a writer, I love the words prologue and epilogue. While this chapter on dating, romance and relationships is now complete, I have a great epilogue for you. I will compare it to a Bruce Springsteen concert. When the concert was over, it wasn't really over. When Bruce and the band left the stage after playing "Born to Run," those of us in the know knew that the real concert was the multi-song encore that Bruce was famous for.

Bruce had his encore and I have my epilogue.

What follows is my version of Bruce Springsteen's encore featuring the Detroit Medley—and if you don't know what that means you missed out on a great life experience!

EPILOGUE

The following are important and relevant concepts for the aging process. I would like to tell you that they're in scientific order—but that would be a lie. Some are more important than others and some may have higher interest to you than to other readers but they all have relevance on the journey.

Memory

Part Three of this series will have detailed chapters on "diseases of the mind" as we age. As for now, a few notes on maintaining your memory as you age. It was shared in Chapter Two that one of the valuable ancillary benefits of writing is improved memory. Start your writing life now. After losing my money clip (holding my license, insurance cards, credit cards, and cash) for the third time, I now only have one place for it in my home. I no longer have to think about where it is. When I return home, the clip goes into one spot; when I leave, I grab it from that spot. One of the best lines ever said about memory is credited to Albert Einstein. "Never commit anything to memory you can simply look up." I have "downloaded" dozens of facts, figures, and statistics from my brain. I know where and how to recall this important information in a matter of seconds from a paper file or computer file. Einstein's advice has helped me tremendously and it will help you.

Meditation

There are many types of meditation (guided, focused, body scan, spiritual, Metta, Chakra, etc.) but the meditation you should practice is Transcendental Meditation. It provides the most benefits for the time you devote to your practice. Stress relief, elimination of fatigue, creativity, and enhanced memory are the main benefits I've received. Many people who think they are meditating are only sitting still for 20 minutes twice per day. The TM Foundation is a non-profit that provides TM to returning military, inner city children, prisoners, etc. It costs money to go through the TM training. A turnoff for many people. But your fee goes to helping others and you are always a part of the TM community once you do the classes. Evidently, it costs more money to learn TM in England than in the U.S. There is a talented English fellow who has made some great TM videos on YouTube. Use your research skills to locate him.

In *Cut Your Calories…Now!!* I wrote about the concept of Mindful Meditation before and during a meal (No. 35 in the list of 40 calorie-cutting ways). The suggestion was to turn off the TV and radio before eating and focus on the meal (it's always OK to have Sinatra on in the background, though). This prevents overeating and helps identify the body signals that you've eaten enough.

But Mindful Meditation isn't really anything specific. TM is. There is a format to the meditation that still allows for flexibility. I haven't researched every form of meditation but there are reasons why TM has achieved the level of acceptance that it has. There is a doctor in my city who gets paid to teach people about Mindful Meditation. He would be better off if he would attend TM training, as would the people he is paid to talk to.

<u>"Spectator Nation"</u>

This is the title of one of my *Post-Gazette* articles. If you were to ask if it was my favorite, my answer would be, "Which of your children do you love the most?" The purpose of the article was to get people to reduce their TV time, screen time, and time watching others participating in sports and become a participant in life. Being a spectator results in less creativity and more calories consumed. Robert Lustig, M.D., an endocrinologist and writer, has a video on YouTube titled "Sugar: The Bitter Truth" with over 11 million views (when I wrote my article, the video had over 4 million views). Dr. Lustig introduced the concept of "buying" your screen time by doing an equal amount of activity time. Instead of watching the local news after dinner (which is really a royal waste of time), use that time for your yoga practice or to take a brisk walk. As I wrote in the article, I can't fault anybody for watching their local sports teams. But I can fault them for watching the pre-game show, the game, and then the post-game show for a discussion by sportscasters discussing what they just saw.

<u>Technology</u>

I used to be the guy afraid of my computer. I paid three different IT people to make my computer faster. They ripped me off. They knew I didn't know basics about computer speed. I have that knowledge now. I came to the realization that I have to stay on the learning curve with technology. I am now proud of my ability to learn about my computers, my phones, my email accounts and the apps that I use. My latest project is to learn as much as I can about my wearable devices. My device measures my time in the pool, time on the bike, and sleep patterns. In the future, everybody will have a wearable device.

One note on managing emails: I love to keep clean email accounts. I delete and unsubscribe (then mark as spam) messages from senders I have no interest in. I have also created files for emails I want to keep. I schedule time during each week to clean my email accounts. They get read and saved, read and deleted, read and filed, read and forwarded, or deleted and unsubscribed. The ones I need to act on, I do so in order of priority.

Downsizing

Just as I downsize my email inboxes, I also downsize research files, clothes, and books on a regular basis. If something can be donated or given to a group or person who could use it, it is. I've donated cold weather gear to Operation Safety Net, a non-profit group providing medical and other services to the homeless in my city. If you have clothes that you're not wearing, get rid of them. I have clients who sold their large homes and downsized into a townhome or large apartment. They had to downsize their possessions. I have other clients who talk about doing it but never seem to get around to it. One thing we should all be downsizing is in the next section.

Grudges

I think everybody has somebody in their history that deserves communication from them. There are grudges that are so old that the relevant parties forgot the original issue. Instead of waiting for the person on the other side of the grudge to contact you, why not extend the olive branch? And don't do it in a text or email. Write a letter or make a telephone call. Better yet, go see the person or call them to arrange a meeting. I know people reading this will agree that it's a good idea with one or two exceptions. They believe they have been aggrieved so badly by somebody that there is just no mending of fences.

One of my Serbian aunts called me some years ago. She was also my godmother. She asked me to do her a favor. When I asked what it was, she said she would be sending me a list of names. Whenever her final day came, I was to make sure these people didn't come to the funeral home. I told her I couldn't do that. I wish I would have told her she needed to make peace with the names on that list. I doubt that she did before she passed away because nobody holds a grudge like a Serbian.

The Only Thing Constant is Change

This was the first line in the first book I wrote. It was a book about the investment industry. The line was a notice to the reader that there were going to be less defined benefit pension plans and more defined contribution plans and that we were all going to have to learn more about the investment business. We would have to be more responsible for our money and our retirement income. For this book, the sentence means that we must accept change, adopt it, and adapt to it. The change in technology has already been discussed. But changes are coming to us all. Our appearance, our careers, the people in our lives, and in our living situations. I mentioned clients who have downsized from a large house to a comfortable townhome or patio home. I probably never realized how difficult that is until I started work on this epilogue. My Uncle John spent the last five years of his life in a state-run veterans home. He left a house that he returned to after WWII and lived in for over 55 years. What was his first night like in that building? What thoughts went through his mind when he was in unfamiliar and uncomfortable surroundings?

Change is coming to us all. Some of it will be negative—another reason to write for the cathartic aspect and to practice TM for the increased ability to deal with life altering changes.

Traveling

One of life's great pleasures and treasures is travel. To do it while you are mobile and healthy is an added bonus. I am lucky to have gotten a lot of traveling in while I was young. I also had great luck because when I went to Cuba, Thailand and Hong Kong, I went with people who were already there or lived there. The luck was that I was able to avoid the dreaded tourist traps and see things I probably wouldn't have seen otherwise. Where do you want to go? I like to ask people if they could wake up in the morning and be in another country, where would they be? I've heard some great answers but I've also heard from people who have zero interest in traveling. These people have extremely limited world visions.

One of the things I love about traveling is the preparation. When I have a trip booked, I put together my reading material weeks before departing. I make a list of the places I want to see. I pack legal pads and material related to any writing project I have in the pipeline. I clean my desk and my office and have my home cleaned. While traveling, I love the thought of knowing I'll be returning to a professionally cleaned place.

In traveling, I think it is important to return to a place you had a great experience in and mix in new locations. I can return to Cuba anytime and my visit will be amazing because I know how to prepare, where to go, and what to avoid. I owe myself a return trip to various towns in the Netherlands related to my interest in art and my WWII-related travel. As for new spots, I hope to travel to South Korea.

I have cousins who grew up in Indianapolis. It was always a great time when they came to Pittsburgh or I went there *(I once saw Sammy Hagar, David Letterman and Paul Newman in quick succession at the Indy 500 track the day before the race)*. One of those cousins recently told me when he retires from his long-term job, he plans to spend a month in Pittsburgh. He'll get a furnished apartment and spend the month touring local museums, places of interest, and spend a lot of time with our relatives. He will also take some day trips to historic places and other destinations within close range. My Indy cousins were always bigger fans of Pittsburgh sports teams than I was. My cousin will come during baseball season so that he can attend Pirates games. His wife will be with him—except at the baseball games!

It is best to do your traveling when you can but this is not always possible. When I was on my last trip to see the Vermeer paintings, my final stop was the National Gallery of Scotland in Edinburgh. "Christ in the House of Martha and Mary" is housed there. I viewed the painting with a museum docent named Rachel. When I shared that this was my 37th and final Vermeer, she told me she had been talking to other Americans. She disappeared for a few moments and came back with an older woman. I was introduced to her by Rachel. Her name was Gertrude and she was from Iowa. She was half bent over, used a cane, and had the look of constipation on her face.

When Rachel told her about my Vermeer journey, Gertrude replied, "I think it's nice that they found that Vermeer in the attic." I calmly explained that if a Vermeer painting had been found in an attic it would be international news. The world would know about it and I would certainly know about it. Gertrude was convinced she heard the story correctly. She called her husband over. Walter had the same bent over walk, same look of constipation and also walked with a cane. He was convinced they saw a news story detailing the discovery of a lost Vermeer. The more I tried to reason with them, the more they were entrenched with the story they think they saw. They were so convinced that a small part of me thought, "Maybe I missed the art story of the century..."

But I hadn't missed it. It didn't happen. Gertrude and Walter were mistaken. When they were younger and working on their Iowa farm, they may have talked about how great it would be to travel across the pond and visit Ireland, England, and Scotland. It was unfortunate for the three of us that we ended up in the National Gallery of Scotland at the same time. It was unfortunate for them that they were only able to do this trip when they were older and had mobility issues. It was unfortunate for me because what should have been a happy moment for me ended up in an embarrassing debate. My moment was overshadowed by a curmudgeonly couple from Iowa and me discussing a Vermeer painting that was not found in somebody's attic.

Learn to Say "No" (and mean it)

Improving your time management skills will mean learning to say the word "No" and standing your ground. Many entities are trying to steal your time. It's up to you to protect this valuable asset. I used to hear "Go there," "Do this," "Buy that," "Read this," "Watch this," all the time. I now have a strong sense of where I want to go, what I want to do, what I want to buy, and what I want to read and watch. I've learned to say "No" to things I won't enjoy or won't add value to my life. When I was younger, I used to let potential clients or potential business associates steal my time. I did a tremendous amount of uncompensated research for individuals who could have afforded to pay me. Now, when somebody suggests I do research on something other than one of my projects, I inform them that the research can be done, and it will be done well, and here is my fee.

Lonely vs. Alone

In my research files, I have various articles detailing a rise in loneliness among middle-aged and older individuals and the negative health effects associated with loneliness. The list of ailments caused by loneliness is not too far from those caused by consistent lack of quality sleep. In my neighborhood there is a wide range of individuals by age, income, and family situation. There are many older individuals walking the streets or sitting in the diners and coffee shops solo. I speak to these people on a regular basis. I'm embarrassed to tell you I never bother to ask their names but I have had many discussions with them. Even the fellow who insists on asking me how I think the Steelers are going to do—at the beginning of baseball season—always gets a good conversation from me. I have noticed that some of the people who I think may have limited social contact seem to "save up" their thoughts and want to present them all at once in a diner conversation. And that's OK with me. If you are out and about and have a sense that somebody in your seating area may be a bit lonely, why not open a conversation with them? I once started a conversation with a gentleman sitting by himself on a bench. He looked beaten up and beaten down. Had the voice of somebody who smoked too many unfiltered Camels and drank too many beers. He told me he had been in the Army with Elvis Presley. I don't know if he was telling the truth or not, but the details of his tale were believable enough to stay with me for a long time. Somebody had to be in the Army with Elvis, right?

I know the difference between loneliness and being alone. A person who writes, by nature of the beast, must spend time alone. I'm fortunate in that I have many acquaintances and clients that are a phone call away. I have a short list of people who are fans of motion pictures and we discuss movies over the phone in detail. I have other people who have insight, experience and common interests I can also call. I know many people—not friends but acquaintances—that I see on a regular basis and enjoy great camaraderie with.

I identify with a quote from Robin Williams. Robin's quote was, "I used to think the worst thing in life was to end up all alone. It's not. The worst thing in life is to end up with people that make you feel all alone." Powerful.

I've been in gatherings with numerous people. The level of the conversations, the types of people, and the amount of people overconsuming alcohol and speaking in repeat mode put me out of my comfort zone. I was lonely. Inversely, I've been alone with reading material, writing projects and movies on DVD or online and I've been 100% content and totally happy. If you're going to write—or travel to Asia on a twenty hour flight—you better be able to occupy yourself for a long period of time.

<u>Holidays</u>

It's not a coincidence that this section follows the one titled Lonely vs. Alone. I've had some of the greatest holiday seasons possible. When I was young and my family was together, the season started after Thanksgiving and lasted into the New Year thanks to the Serbian holidays. I've spent five Christmases and New Year's Eves in Cuba. I don't have the writing skills to detail what that was like. When I was with my ex-fiancée and her daughter we did the school plays, the light up nights, the trips to the miniature railroad at the Carnegie Science Center (only Pittsburgh readers will appreciate that reference), ice skating sessions, and the wrapping and exchanging of gifts. Those were phenomenal holiday seasons. I've also had holiday seasons where I was alone—and a bit lonely—with not much going on in my life. But even in those tough seasons, I had the memories of great holidays past and I also used the end of the year to get a "game plan" together for the upcoming year. There were times in December when I overbought, overdrank and did things I wouldn't have done in the months of April, June, or October. But I didn't have the proper skills to get through those tough holiday seasons. Please use the coping skills I have used (yet another endorsement for writing) to get yourself through any tough holiday season.

There was a local radio personality who overcame alcoholism before he started his radio career in Florida. He got a job in Pittsburgh and was a general talk show host on a few different stations for many years. I remember him talking about sitting in his apartment by himself on Christmas Eve listening to Christmas music, thinking about past Christmases with tears streaming down his face. He said he wasn't sad. He said the feeling he had was one of bittersweetness.

We won't have movie-like or TV commercial-like Christmas seasons. Some of us will have recently deceased relatives, estranged family, and will be spending our days in a less than productive, creative, happy way. Some of us will not have a romantic partner due to divorce, death or—worse yet—bad online dating skills (pardon the attempt at humor). Don't let the commercialization of the season impact your demeanor and behavior.

In Chapter Ten, I shared my friend's idea for the Holiday Matchmaking service. My friend never pursued the idea, and I have no interest in the idea (but love the concept). If you're an enterprising person, feel free to take the idea and make it a business. It will certainly keep you busy and occupied during the holiday season.

While we're here, let's collectively do something that needs done. Let's do away with, "Are you ready for the holidays?" and "How were your holidays?" What does the first one even mean? I've been asked that question two days after Halloween. As for the second one, it's a tough question to answer for somebody who just went through a tough holiday season. I was in a local diner one year a few days after the first of the year. A young man known to the owners and customers was a homeless alcoholic. He was a super sweet guy. He would bus tables in exchange for a meal. He was at the counter. A regular customer asked him how his holidays were. The young man replied, "I'm homeless and I'm an alcoholic. How do you think my holidays were?" For many reasons, let's all stop asking those two pointless questions.

Glory Days

I used to bite my lip when one of my friends would talk about a sporting event they participated in years, if not decades, previous. I would think those people were living in the past. One of my favorite Glory Days stories concerns a fellow from a family I grew up with. Big family. The oldest son, about seven years older than me, was a great baseball player. He was a pitcher. I never knew him to play any other sport but he could "throw that speedball by you; make you look like a fool, boy." He told me years ago that when he was playing in the Federation League (the top league before the minor leagues) that the Pirates and the Astros scouted him. A few years later, he told me the Pirates, the Astros and the Orioles had scouted him. A few years after that, he told me the Pirates, the Astros, the Orioles and the Blue Jays had scouted him. I told him if we both lived long enough, all major league teams would have scouted him, including the expansion teams that weren't in existence when he was playing!

I've changed my opinion about sharing Glory Days stories. Keeping these stories in our memory may help keep that memory active. My sports career ended before it should have due to my back injury and spinal surgery. I've got some cool stories of my own that I like to share.

Where I do draw the line, however, is when the same person tells me the same story for the fourth time. Three times is my limit. I'm good with three. I have a friend who was a top wrestler in high school. He was in some big matches. He would tell me the same stories over and over. We now have a mutually agreed upon word that I use if he starts with a rerun of one of his stories. Since we implemented the word (it's a four-syllable word that really isn't a dictionary word; our metal shop teacher used it) I haven't heard the stories that I've heard enough times.

One of my favorite Glory Days stories concerns one of the coolest actions I've ever seen. We had a wrestling match at McKeesport High School. It was going to be in front of the student body. It was a cold, cold January day. We were in the auditorium before the match. Coach Harding was giving us a pre-match speech. Suddenly, the back door opened and a young man was standing there—shirtless and cut like a pro body builder. He asked who wrestled in the 145-pound weight class. Our wrestler at 145 sunk lower in his chair. Another wrestler stood up and told the kid he was the 145-pound wrestler (he wasn't) and asked "What about it?" The shirtless kid said "See you on the mat." My teammate shot back, "We can take care of business right here right now." Coach Harding told the young man who cut in on his speech to get back to his class. I was in awe. It was such a great moment that I used it in a script I wrote about high school wrestling. A few years ago, I saw the teammate who had stood up and challenged the McKeesport wrestler. It had been decades since the event happened. When I told him that I used that event in a script, he had no memory of what I was talking about. That was of interest to me. I can share, in great detail, plays I made on a baseball field or a football practice field more than 40 years ago that weren't nearly as interesting as what I witnessed at McKeesport High School. Yet, the author of that cool event didn't even remember it.

Breakfast Clubs

Connected to Glory Days is the concept of breakfast clubs. All over my city retired and semi-retired individuals gather at diners and coffee shops to discuss topical events, local sports teams and their own stories. I was involved in such a group with clients of mine. Due to changes in working and new homes being built, we meet only on occasion. I've been in places where I can identify such groups gathering. I know of a group of retired bricklayers meeting in one spot, retired city workers in another and various spots where veterans meet. I think these clubs are a good idea. It gives individuals who may not have full schedules somewhere to be on certain days at a certain time—and be around friendly people. If you are a member of such an unofficial group, or start one, proper conversation rules apply. Talk half as much as you listen. Ask sincere questions to those who are on the sideline. Get them involved. And no discussion of politics (a rule my breakfast club broke all the time) and religion.

High School Reunions

I shared in Chapter Ten that there were 972 students in my high school class. We were a diverse, talented, athletic, artistic group with the proper number of stoners thrown in for color. I did not attend the first two reunions. I knew the organizers and knew the events would be "beer fests". The reunion committee hired an outside vendor for the 15-year reunion. That company, after collecting checks and credit card information from a number of my classmates, went bankrupt. Heading into our 20-year reunion, those who lost money five years previous were upset about it. I was cajoled into being a volunteer for the 20-year reunion. Not only did we have aggrieved classmates who had lost money, but the high school lost our class roster. We had to resurrect a list of students plus obtain current addresses. There were a number of volunteers alongside me to do this.

I learned some valuable life lessons from this project. Most people I contacted didn't know who I was. Granted, I missed most of 11th grade due to my back surgery, but there were people I knew fairly well and they insisted they didn't know me even after I told them about mutual friends we had and parties we attended together. There were a number of people who didn't want to be contacted for our 20-year reunion and any that followed.

The committee had numerous meetings in a local bar. We all got drunk and told stories. I realized that some of the married members of the committee were using the reunion planning as a way to get out of the house for a few nights. I didn't appreciate that then but certainly do now. There was something else going on at these meetings that bothered me.

I overheard classmates talking about the physical changes in other classmates, and not in a positive way. Most of the whispering was about weight gain for the women and hair loss with weight gain for the men. I had already been involved in my self-study in the fields of nutrition and fitness and was aware of the importance of the Genetic Lottery, although I wasn't using that term at the time.

At one of the meetings, before we had too much to drink, I stood up and asked to make a short statement. I told my classmates that I didn't appreciate the conversations about the physical changes to other classmates. We were going to be the "kind and accepting" class. I went on to say that much of what we look like is beyond our control and we don't know what other variables were at play. Classmates could have had an illness, had children and parents with health issues and could have had other stressful situations in life. I don't think my plea did any good, but I was glad I stood and delivered it.

When the actual reunion happened, we had fewer than 120 people, including spouses. Such a large class but such low attendance at the reunion. Even though I had delivered my speech about acceptance, I was surprised how radically different some people looked just 20 years after high school. It was amazing to me how the human form can change so much—or so little—for a group of people of the same age. Those who had been smoking cigarettes since high school had the added disadvantage of changes in their skin and teeth.

I would suggest this if you plan to go to a reunion: do not drink alcohol. This would be a perfect time to remain in control while those around you are getting inebriated, louder, and entrenching themselves in Repeat Mode. Talk to the people you knew well, and let them do most of the talking. Introduce—or reintroduce—yourself to people whose names you knew from school but didn't have interaction with. Stay away from those who are using "I" too much and talking about their lofty position in life as if "time, place, and circumstance" wasn't the main reason for it.

Final note on reunions: I've now attended six of them. The day after each, I woke up feeling slightly depressed. That feeling is caused by a mixture of the depressive-nature of alcohol and the realization that the reunion I just attended will never take place again and I was now one step closer to the end.

Talking to People Younger Than Yourself

When I was younger, few things ticked me off as much as when an older person would say, "You should…" or "If I was you…." These people would then dispense their value-less opinions. They had no insight or real-world experience that had any relevance to my situation, my time in life, or my ambition. They felt because they were older that they had some insight. And they didn't. Just worthless opinions. Much of the time, if it was a family member, I had to bite my tongue and listen to the advice politely as I didn't want to upset my parents, who were most times close by. So, when I talk to people younger than myself, I never disrespect them by saying, "If I was you…." or "You should…" or "What you need to do…" When my stepdaughter and other young people have asked me what I think they should study in college, my answer is twofold. (1) Study something they have passion for and hope for continued passion and (2) Study as if you are going to be an entrepreneur. I've also told younger people the importance of improving their writing and public speaking abilities and the importance of opening their world vision through traveling.

When my stepdaughter was much younger and we got into a situation where she wanted to do something that her mother or myself didn't think appropriate, or she said something that was a little off key, I would tell her that she was thinking with a "12-year-old brain" because that's what she was working with. That when she had a 16-year-old brain, or a 22-year-old brain, she would she the world differently because her world view will have changed. I think the idea of how we see the world based on our age and the accompanying insight, experience and knowledge is a valid concept to share with people of all ages.

A young man in a bar made a derogatory comment to me concerning my age. I didn't get mad at him but I was prepared. I told him it is true that he is, in fact, younger than me but I had no choice in when I came into this world and that I made good use of my time. I told him about my business ventures, my travel history, my writing, my nocturnal exploits and my future endeavors. I asked him what he would be doing with the next 25 years of his life. What businesses will he start? What creative endeavors will he produce? What romantic interludes will he experience? Will he ever take a trip out of our state—let alone the country? I then told him that he would trade the next 25 years of his life for my memories—and the photos stored on my phone.

Avoid the One Big Muck-Up

As an investment professional, I read various industry newsletters. On a regular basis, I read about "brokers gone bad". It is typically an older individual with high net worth clients who decides he or she needs more money for themselves than what they've earned. They do something unethical, immoral and—often—illegal to convert their clients' money into theirs. Some of these practices have gone on for years but the brokers eventually get caught. When I read these reports, I wonder two things: Did the broker think they would never get caught? How did they sleep at night knowing what they did to people who entrusted them with their money?

You must avoid the One Big Muck-Up in your business or in your family life when you're well into the Third Act. Forget about just the shame you would bring to yourself; think about the shame you will bring to your extended family members.

In the era of "ride-share," nobody should get a DUI. A fellow I knew from the exercise facility I used to attend liked to leave the job he hated on Friday and stop for a night of drinking. Unfortunately, the place he stopped at was far from his house. He was told by many people many times that he shouldn't be in a bar for a few hours drinking high alcohol content beer and then driving home. His number came up one night and he was pulled over by the police. He rang up his first DUI at the age of 55. The embarrassment, coupled with the fact he had a job he hated (I know the company he worked for and what his job duties were. I fully understood his hatred of the job) sunk him. A few months after getting the DUI, he took his life, leaving behind elderly parents, siblings, nieces, and nephews.

The Greatest Late in Life Muck-Up Ever? That's easy. Salvatore "Sal" Tessio's betrayal of Michael Corleone. What was that guy thinking? Bringing Michael to Brooklyn for a supposed friendly meeting with two men who wanted him dead and the Corleone family eliminated? All the history he had with the Corleones, and all the good memories he created weren't going to get Tessio out of that royal muck-up. Don't "Tessio" yourself late in life.

<u>Family Matters</u>

I am friends with sets of siblings. Yet, those siblings aren't friends with each other. Something or some things happened in their upbringing that put them on the outs. I get along famously with each sibling but whatever happened in their history has kept them on less than brotherly terms. Inversely, most people from my neighborhood went to the same beer parties in Elm Leaf Park, smoked marijuana and knew the bars where you could get served underage. Half of the people who did that went on to having a regular, productive life and the other half (figuratively speaking) stayed in those bars.

There is a surprisingly high number of guys I grew up with, and played baseball with and against, who are either dead or have their life marked by substance abuse. I know or knew the parents and siblings of many of those dead or constantly drunk. And you know what? Their parents were solid people. Their siblings were solid people. What happened? Here's the answer: the time, place and circumstances where we all grew up. Society and environmental factors have powerful influence over a person's upbringing, sometimes more powerful than a stable, solid family.

Not every child will be the same pride and joy to you when they reach adulthood as when they were youngsters. And it won't be your fault. I came up at a time when cocaine was prevalent in my city. Many young people who came from good homes and good families got tripped up by the "nose whiskey". It was not a reflection of the parents or the home life. It was just an example of time, place, and circumstance.

I once told my stepdaughter that her parents, her grandparents, and me would be doing our collective best to keep her on the right track by sharing our experiences and hoping that she didn't make the same mistakes we made. I know that's good advice but not sure if it's realistic. Younger people will push the envelope, experiment, use a 22-year-old brain to make their decisions and, as a result, make the same mistakes we made. We can only hope they survive those mistakes as we did, learn from them, and not repeat them (so that they can tell the young people coming up behind them not to make the same mistakes!).

Dealing with the Media

In "Spectator Nation," I made the comment one should not waste time watching the local news. And, if anything, my opinion on the subject has gotten more concrete. It's not that it's just an inefficient way to obtain news, many of the stories aren't really stories. As a person interested in medicine, nutrition, and fitness, I have seen numerous stories on those subjects, promoted before the newscast and during the newscast ("Stay tuned for the new way to lose 10 pounds!"). When the story airs, the information provided is not specific, has been aired before, comes from a study often financed by an entity with financial motivation, and always ends the same way: "Researchers say further studies are needed." (They say that as a way to get the researchers more money.)

When it comes to issues of finance and investing, I tell my clients the same thing: when there is a story about investing on the local news, and a seller of investment products is interviewed, what they don't tell you is usually more important than what they do tell you. I'm going to use a quote from John Kenneth Galbraith here. Galbraith was not only a great economist but he was an equally great writer—a beautiful combination. In matters of media and investing, Galbraith once said, "Pundits forecast not because they know, but because they are asked."

At any age, the media is not the best source for objective, unbiased information. There is a profit motive to the information being presented.

How To Be Old

THE SECOND EPILOGUE

There were a few Springsteen concerts I attended where Bruce and the band left the stage after the encore—only to return for a second encore. So, what you have here is The Second Epilogue.

The greatest television series in the history of TV is HBO's *The Wire*, the series detailing the police and drug dealers in Baltimore. The second-best series was *Band of Brothers*, the story of Easy Company's 506th Parachute Infantry Regiment and their experiences from preparing to go to war, to landing in Normandy on D-Day, to fighting their way across France, the Netherlands and Belgium, and being in Germany when the war ended.

I was so influenced by *Band of Brothers* that when I went to the Netherlands, I flew to Belgium, rented a car and drove to Bastogne, key location in the Battle of the Bulge. I visited the villages in and around this part of Belgium. One of the highlights of my traveling career is stopping at the sight of a large black marble monument. I parked and walked across the street. The landscaping around the monument let me know it was relatively new. The monument simply read, "This is for the Brothers who didn't come home." I had tears in my eyes when I saw that inscription and I have some right now as I'm writing about it. Episode Six of *Band of Brothers* deals with Bastogne. This part of The Second Epilogue deals with Episode Three, "Carentan".

In this episode, we're introduced to a soldier named Albert Blithe. Blithe was representative of the many soldiers who had difficulty in war because they couldn't function as frontline troops (an estimate from Charles Glass' 2013 book, *The Deserters: A Hidden History of WWII,* is that 50,000 soldiers deserted in the European Theater alone). Private Blithe shares that when he landed in Normandy, he found a ditch, got in it, and went to sleep. Before the Battle of Carentan, one week after the Normandy landing (D Day+ 6), Blithe develops "hysterical blindness" which temporarily sidelines him. Blithe is counseled by Lt. Ronald Speirs who is All-Army all the time. He is a soldier's soldier.

Speirs calmly tells Blithe what he needs to do in order to function as a solider. What Blithe's problem is, according to Speirs, is that he is still thinking that there is hope he will survive the war. Speirs tells him, "The only hope you have is to accept the fact you're already dead. Accept that and you can function."

You've read my chapter on religion and my belief in what the afterlife is. When I heard the advice Speirs gave to Blithe, it resonated with me. What I was saying—or trying to say in that chapter—is that we're all out of here one day. So, while we're here, let's make good use of our time, clear our respective bucket lists, do our best to create, achieve, accomplish, do good deeds, and help others when we can.

You should never accept a life situation by thinking, "Things aren't so great here and now but when I die, I'm going to be welcomed to a better place and every day will be perfect." Because if you think objectively, use your good common sense, realize that in the history of the earth over 100 billion people have already lived and died, you may come around to my way of thinking. This is all there is. The afterlife is the good works, influences and love you leave behind. If people talk about you in a positive way after you're gone, you're still here.

A note about Albert Blithe. In the "Carentan" episode, he is shown, after Speirs' advice and some encouragement by Easy Company commander First Lieutenant Dick Winters, firing his rifle in battle. We are led to believe he shoots and kills a German, as we see that soldier's helmet rolling down the hill. Later in the episode, with his newly found courage, Blithe volunteers to approach a farm house. Right before he advances on the house, he is shot in the neck. He is pulled out of harm's way by members of his platoon. At the end of the episode, we read that Blithe died in 1948 as a result of the wound he suffered. Not true. Albert Blithe's wound put him out of WWII but he returned to see service in the Korean War and was on active duty in Germany in 1967 where he died from a perforated ulcer and not a German bullet.

The Final Word (for Part One, anyway)

The year 1939 was probably the greatest year for motion picture releases. *Gone with the Wind, Mr. Smith Goes to Washington, The Wizard of Oz, Gunga Din* (and others) were all released during that year.

Also debuting that year was a Broadway play that would receive the Pulitzer Prize for Drama and the New York Drama Critics Circle Award. The play was written by William Saroyan and was titled *The*

Time of Your Life. The title of the play comes from this quote: "In the time of your life—live." I cut the quote short for my purpose, but I can't think of any other sentence that will best end Part One of *How To Be Old*.

See you with Part Two...

Suggested reading:

An excellent precursor to *How To Be Old* is *Cut Your Calories…Now!!* As shared in the Introduction, it was immediately after writing CYCN that how I got the idea for HTBO.

You can access *Cut Your Calories…Now!!* as a printed book or eBook on the Amazon platform.

Ken Kaszak

Printed in Great Britain
by Amazon

29011872R00097